CODES & CIPHERS

Also in this series:

Mystery Puzzles by Chris M. Dickson

Mind Benders: Adventures in Lateral Thinking by David J. Bodycombe

Optical Illusions & Picture Puzzles by David J. Bodycombe

Devised by
David J. Bodycombe

With an introduction by
Victor Serebriakoff
Hon. President of International MENSA

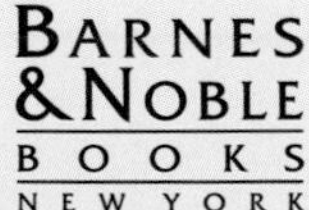

This edition published by Barnes & Noble, Inc.,
by arrangement with Constable & Robinson Ltd.

The use of copyright clipart originated by Corel Corporation, Techpool Studios Inc., One Mile Up Inc., and Image Club Graphics Inc., is acknowledged.

2002 Barnes & Noble Books

ISBN 0 7607 2897 6

Printed and bound in Singapore

01 02 03 M 9 8 7 6 5 4 3 2

INTRODUCTION

By Victor Serebriakoff,
Hon. President of International MENSA

The encryption of information is an ancient art which probably came with the very first phonetic writing, which is reputed to have been in cuneiform symbols marked in clay. This came even before the Egyptian ideograms, which we see revived today in the form of "icons" in Information Technology. An ideogram is in essence a small formalized picture of the object or event to be communicated.

The reason why ideograms cannot easily be encrypted is that there are so many of them. Each one is unique and represents a concept or percept, rather than the sounds we make to convey the meaning. It would be hard to find a consistent way of encoding such complex symbols.

The problem of the cryptographer is to deceive or to uncover deception. In the case of the examples set within these pages, their intention is to hide from you the information you seek, the hidden message which lies hidden within the riddle.

The whole art of encryption, as well as the opposite art of decryption, has been revolutionized by the invention of the first computers. They were first used at Bletchley Park in Southern England by mathematician Alan Turing during World War Two to break the German military and naval codes. This is claimed to have ensured the victory of the Allies in that war.

The German encoding machine was ingenious. It encoded the letters of the alphabet as other letters, but the same letter was encrypted differently each time, thus defeating the simple method of code breaking, that based on letter frequency. There is then the more arduous method, that of trying every mechanical coding procedure systematically. That is almost impossible for the unaided solver, although much simpler with a computer to do the donkey work. But because the German machine changed the code with each letter, the work was too arduous even for a computer.

The answer which Turing and the big team of brilliant people around him found exploited the individual weaknesses of the enemy radio operators. All the encrypted broadcasts were sent in Morse code, and it was possible for a good British operator to recognize the "handwriting" or personal Morse style of the individual enemy operators. Furthermore, the principle of the coding machine, although not the initial setting for each transmission, was known to the code-breakers.

With that information, certain routine messages (like signing-off and signing-on signals) could be decrypted. With such clues to guide them, and the ability to try many combinations in a short time which Turing's early machines provided, the decryption specialists gradually shortened the time needed to solve the codes to the point where the information gained was useful.

In practice, it was also possible for Japanese codes to be broken, despite their ideogram-based language. In order to encode their massages, the Japanese devised a phonetic way of conveying meaning because, in those early days, radio telegraphy had to use a Morse-type code. The days of the bit-map transmission, such as facsimile, were a long way in the future.

I am sure I can promise the bold and fearless reader who tackles these codes and ciphers many hours of happy absorption. In particular, I have no doubt you will enjoy the instant feeling when you suddenly see through the wily trickery and get the right answer.

There's a particular bird that, in recent months, has been spotted flying across the United States of America, from the West coast to the East.

This bird made a number of scheduled stops for a few nights before continuing its journey. The numbers on the map show you the states in which it rested.

By solving the hidden code, you will be able to identify the type of bird.

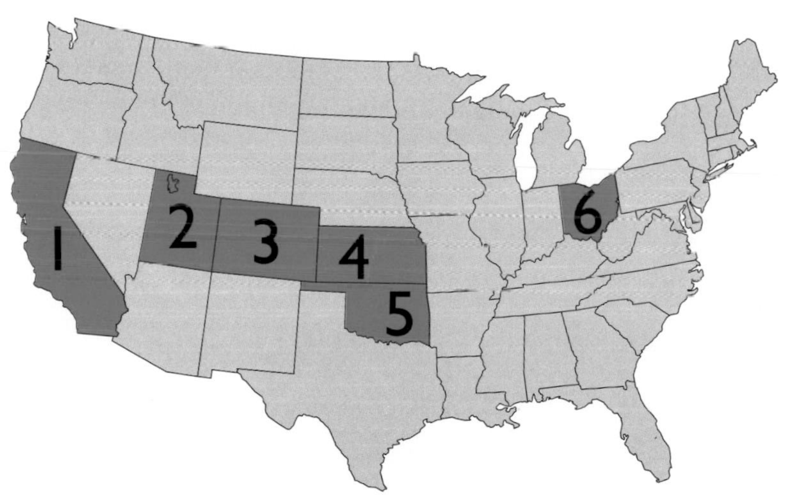

Use the clues provided to solve the code.

CLUE 1. One diagonal spells **IOU** (in some direction).

CLUE 2. One row spells **TOO** backwards.

CLUE 3. Both **T**s have a vowel in the square above them and in the square to their left.

CLUE 4. When the puzzle is completed, one square remains blank.

CLUE 5. **Y** and **G** are in adjacent squares.

The solution to this code is before your very eyes. The diagram holds the key.

You should be able to solve this one pretty quickly, especially if you have a thick felt-tip pen handy.

As an expert cryptologist (even after only three puzzles), you have been hired by the Government to crack the safe shown below.

The safe was found in a secret location, and is believed to contain valuable secrets. All that is known about this kind of safe is that the code sequence is four shapes long, and that the final shape must be the circle.

What sequence would you use to open the safe?

In this puzzle, a friend is testing your ability to look for information that you can't see.

You arrive at the hotel which is to be your home for the next week. A knock at the door – "Parcel for you," says the bellboy. You tip him and open the package. In it you find an invitation and a calculator. The invitation says "Sarah's Birthday Party. 8 for 8.30 pm. Hotel Grande Restaurant. For dress code, see enclosed." The calculator is on and displays the number 731.

How would you dress for the occasion?

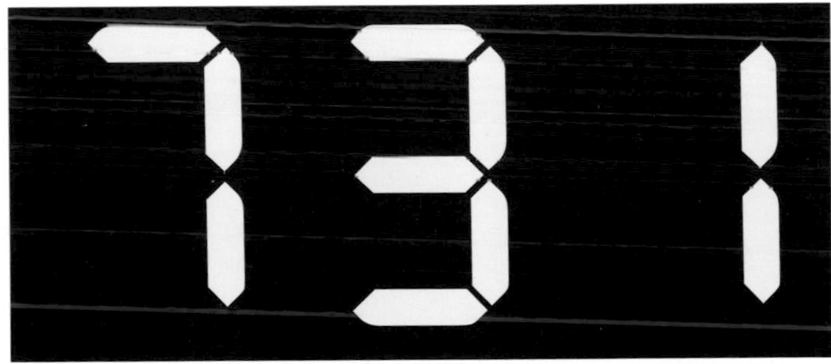

There is a prize in one of these boxes, and the others are empty. There is nothing to distinguish one box from another apart from the symbols on the top of the boxes.

Some of these boxes have something in common, whether it be the shade or meaning of the symbol. See if you can find the significance of this fact, which will ultimately reveal the location of the correct box.

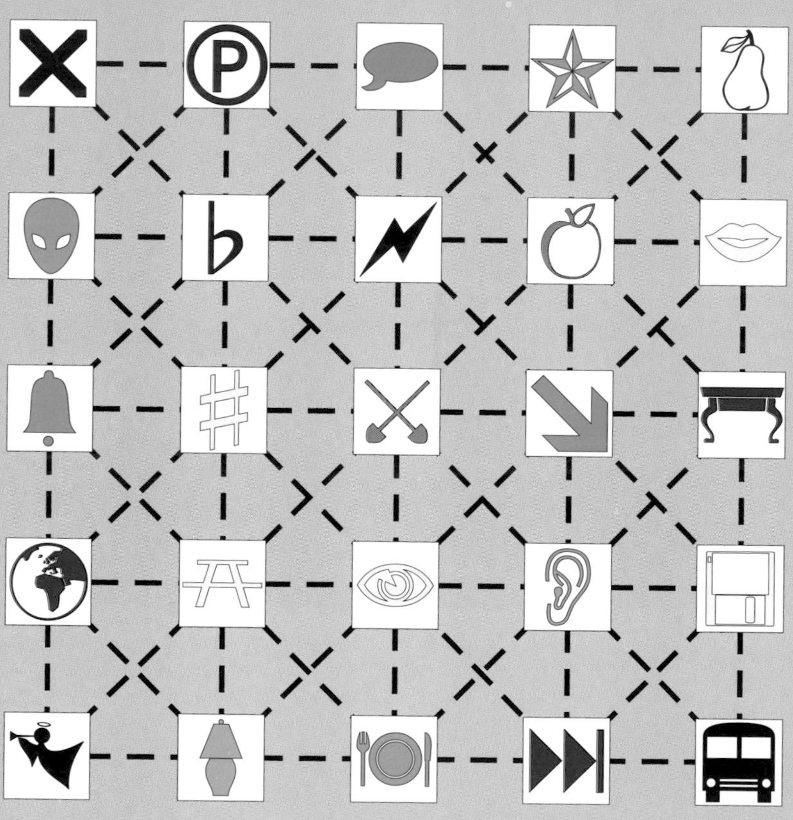

Your mission is to meet a secret agent in a certain hotel. When you book in at the foyer, the receptionist hands you an envelope.

Retiring to the comfort of your own room, you open the envelope to find a piece of paper and some shapes which look like letters cut in half. Some of the shapes have already been arranged to look like FTCFIX, but there are four spare pieces left over. The piece of paper says "Meet me at this room".

By substituting the four spare pieces for four from the given letters, and a little further rearrangement, can you discover which hotel room is your rendezvous?

A puzzle that needs no introduction... literally. Both the question and answer are contained in this grid.

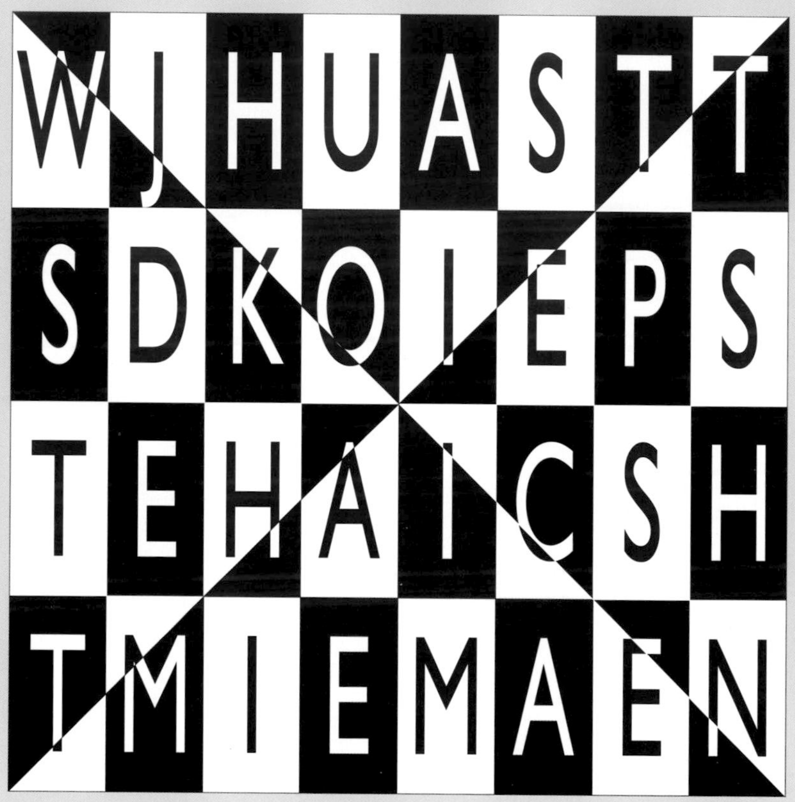

Two puzzles for the price of one. Use the diagram to decode the encrypted message below. Then see if you can solve the subsequent puzzle that will become apparent.

UD "RTOWQEURWE" UA
BIR RGW IBKT KIBFWAR
QIES YAUBF KWRRWEA
DEIN RGW RIO EIQ,
RGWB RGW IRGWEA
NYAR VW...?

You need to gain access beyond a door which blocks your path. The door is secured via a standard four-digit combination lock, where all the digits are between 1 and 9.

Your operatives in the field have been able to gather certain clues about the identity of the code, but now it's up to you to complete the job.

What code will gain you access?

YELLOW = The average of all four digits

RED = Sum of yellow and green digits

GREEN = Number of letters in yellow digit

BLUE = Difference between green and blue digits

Rearrange these blocks to find out what code phrase you must use when you are meeting your secret contact.

As a hint, in the correct solution the two Ys, Os and Ns are in adjacent squares.

Your aim is to find an eight-digit combination, and the only clues you have been provided with are the words below.

Your back-up team have managed to find out that the sequence begins "54...". Using this as a starting point, can you deduce the combination?

1 CREDIT CARD

2 TYPEWRITER

3 CALCULATOR

4 Ρανσομ Νοτε

5 RUBBER STAMP

6 OLD COMPUTER

7 GREEK

8 HANDWRITING

You are playing hangman with an opponent and, sadly, you haven't done too well so far.

However, I know what the answer is. Using the diagrams shown, and given that there is no letter "Z" in the word, see if you can work out the winning word.

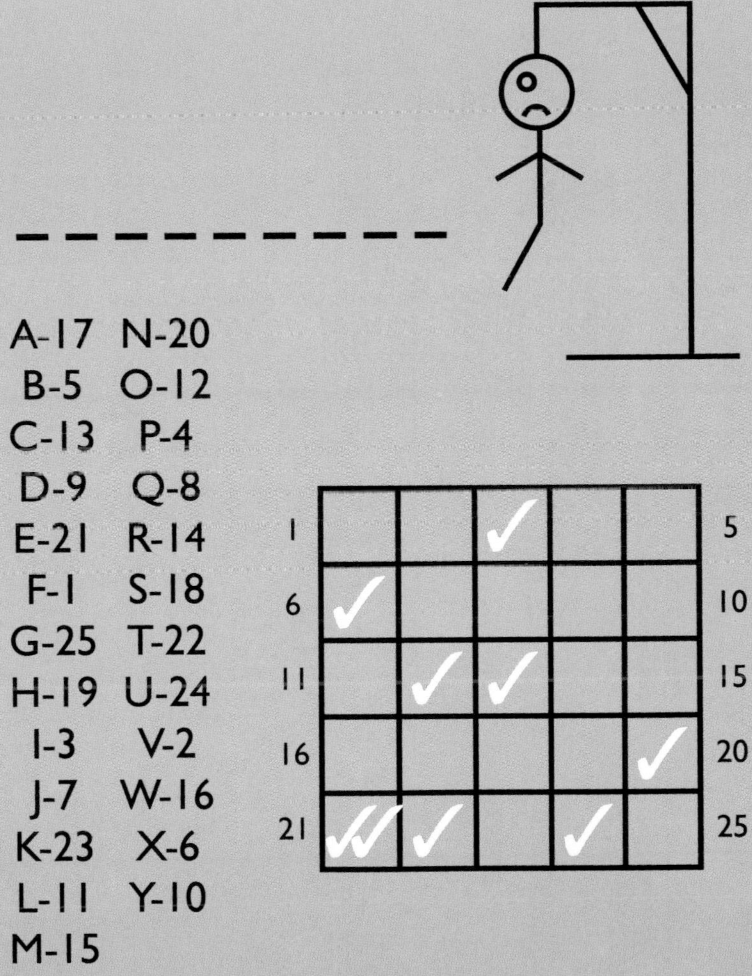

This grid contains a very important secret message. Find out what this message is by changing direction as you travel through the grid.

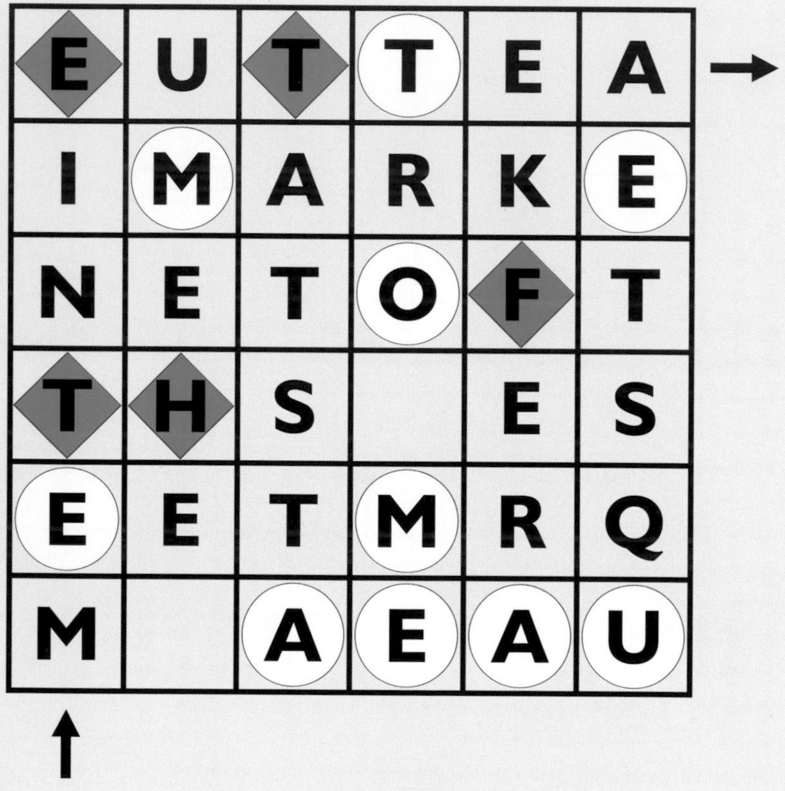

Your itinerary for a trip around the United States has been handed to you. In order to maintain its secrecy, it has been encoded.

Can you deduce where you are headed for over the next few days?

Get to Florida by air __ ____ _r sea. From there, follow up the East coast. This will be the only place with a suitable laundry for quite some time, so make sure you do your _______ ___ight. Then head further North, but take care: there will be a lot of tramps and ho___ ___ight. Then head almost directly West to a big city where many of the residents are rebellious in open spaces (technically known as anar___ ___raphobics). Then travel South to have something to eat. Try salami in focaccia bread, which is a sand____ ___lians like to eat. Then continue South to the border, where you must complete your mission by offering assistance. You must h___ _ __n of a Mexican father. Then return to base.

While touring Europe, you are approached by a woman in the street. "You are needed. Ring this number as soon as possible," she pleads. She hands you a newspaper bearing the message shown below, before disappearing into the crowd once more.

You go into the nearest telephone box to make your call. What number would you dial?

FOR TOOTH, I'VE
ATE NIGH – NATO.

You must find out the enemy's secret codeword using the diagram we have managed to obtain for you. However, they have been extremely cunning by using a code which seems incredibly abstract.

However, with a bit of lateral thinking you should be able to deduce the nine-letter word required.

A short communication is encoded here. The key to this puzzle is to use the blocks shown and place them in the grid provided.

Can you overcome the odds and discover the message?

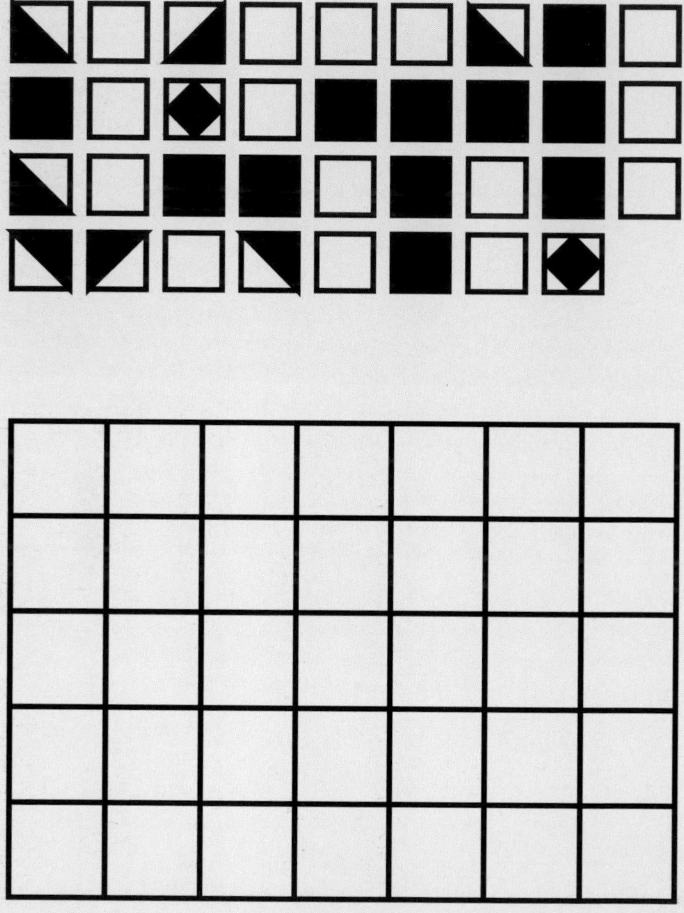

This puzzle looks perfectly ordinary, and yet it contains a very helpful code. Watch carefully. Look at both images and see what you can find. If you are clever enough, you will discover a cipher that will contain the answer to this question. If you do not understand, then fear not. The solution is, as ever, in the answers section of the book. But first, see if you can solve it without the answer.

This puzzle looks
perfectly ordinary, and
yet it contains a very
helpful code. Watch
carefully. Look at both
mages and see what
you can find. If you are
clever enough, you will
discover a cipher that
will contain the answer
to this question. If you
do not understand,
then fear not. The
solution is, as ever, in
the answers section of
the book. But first, see
if you can slve it
without the answer.

The diagram shows the dial of a safe. Not a great deal is known about the combination, but we have managed to gain a few clues. We don't know the correct starting position, but we do know that the number of "clicks" after each letter is five, then eight, then eleven, changing direction each time.

Also, the correct combination spells out a four-letter word. What is this word?

Another codeword puzzle, but this one looks like it's a mathematical equation.

Two forms of encryption have taken place – one is straightforward, the other less so.

Can you calculate the correct answer?

You are trying to disarm this atomic model. Eleven of the atoms are neutral, but one is charged. You have to work out which one is the rogue and remove it.

Which is the dangerous atom, and what is so "neutral" about the other eleven letters?

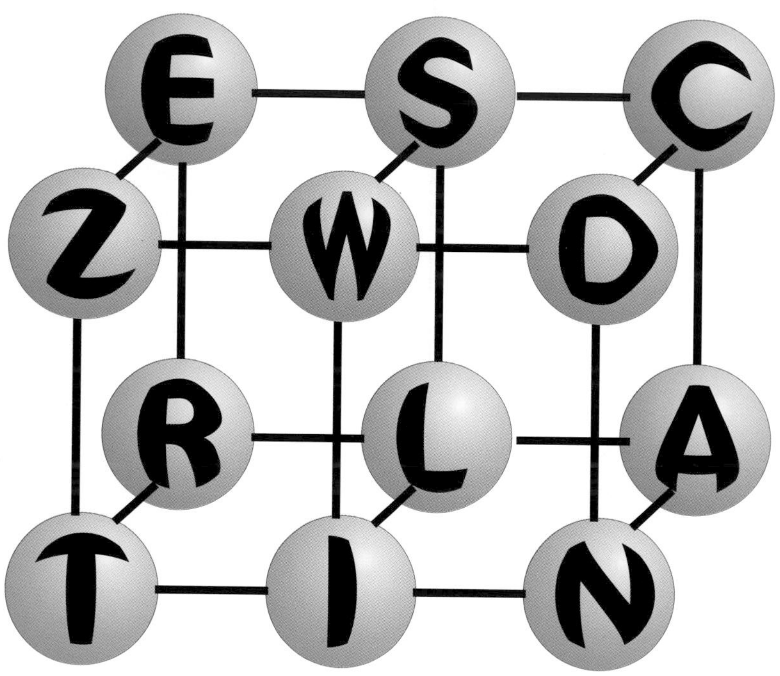

This is a decoding machine which takes in a set of seven letter tiles and produces a word. It does this by revolving the wheel through a half-turn, then moving the tiles two positions along, and repeating until the word is decoded.

What word does the following become when decoded using the machine? Guessers beware – there are many possible anagrams of these letters!

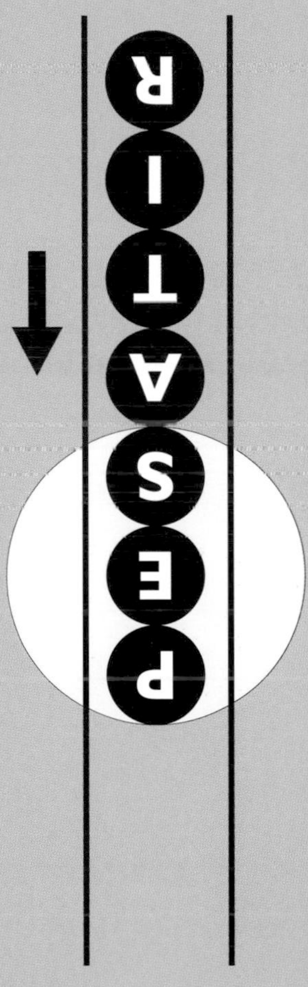

By looking at this diagram carefully, and using a little foresight, you can spell out a simple message.

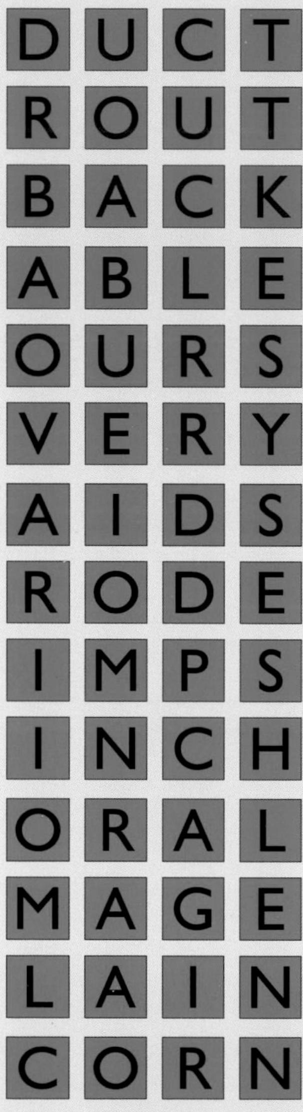

1) If Vulcan was the Roman god of fire, cross out the E; otherwise cross out the A.

2) If the River Kwai is found in Singapore, cross out the C; otherwise cross out the M.

3) If *Revolver* and *Rubber Soul* are titles of Beatles albums, cross out the S; otherwise cross out the N.

4) If Pluto is the coldest planet in the Solar System, cross out the P; otherwise cross out the Y.

5) If an eagle means "two under par" in golf, cross out the T; otherwise cross out the R.

6) If an icosahedron is a solid figure made from twenty hexagons, cross out the O; otherwise cross out the I.

What word remains?

What secret do these blocks of yellow and red lights hide?

There are three additional anagrams of the word DECLAIM. Work out what they are, and then place the letters in the diamonds so that all four words can be spelled out by following the black lines.

On your latest mission, you are trying to break in to a top-security lab but unfortunately a word-lock blocks your path. You know that this variety of combination requires a seven-letter word where every button is used at least once.

With lightning-quick thought, you deduce that one of the buttons must be used twice. It transpires that one particular button, if pressed twice, will make the door impossible to open. This is because a suitable word cannot be formed using two instances of that letter.

Which of the six buttons is this?

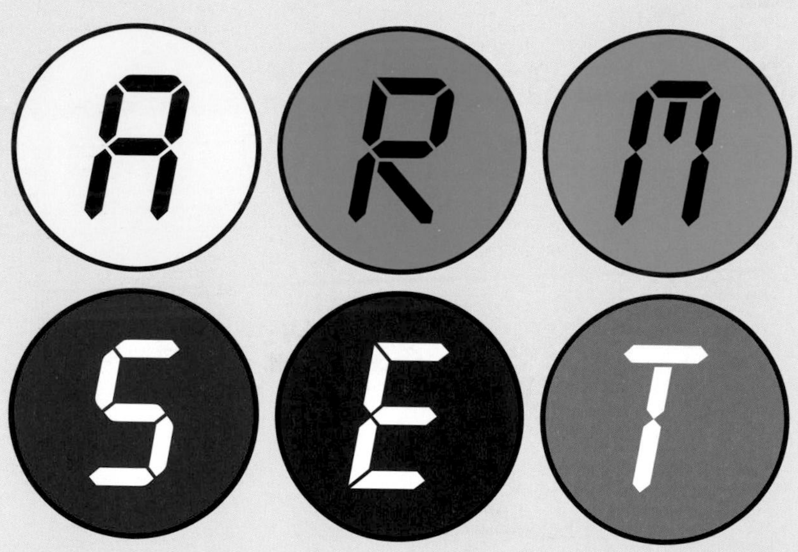

Your next challenge is a little more sedentary. All you have to do is complete this crossword. There are a few letters already in the grid to start you off.

What are you waiting for? Oh, I've forgotten the clues. Never mind – I'm sure you'll find another way to solve the puzzle.

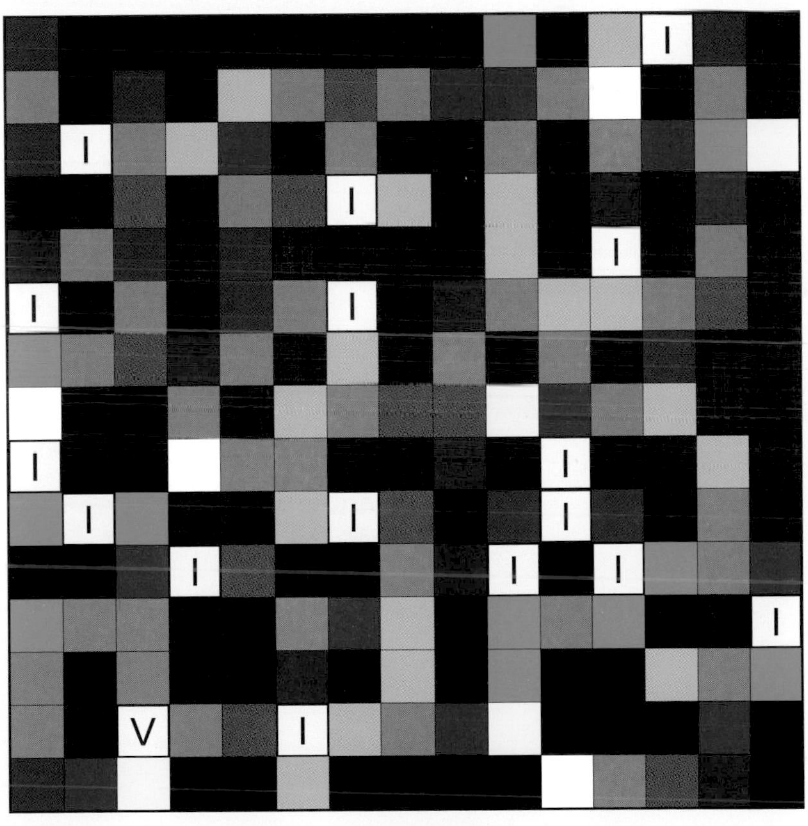

This is one of those alphabet arithmetic (or "alphametic") puzzles where each different digit is represented by a different letter of the alphabet. The alphabet version is shown first, followed by the arithmetic version underneath.

I have revealed the positions of some numbers, and all the occurrences of the letters of C, O, D and E. The key on the left is incomplete, but is listed in alphabetical order. When you are finished, something familiar should be apparent.

With thanks to Chris Cole

?=7
?=1
C=8
D=3
E=4
?=5
?=9
O=2
?=0
?=6

```
    D???D
X    DDDC
---------
?OD?CO??E
```

```
    3???3
X    3338
---------
?23?82??4
```

Each row contains the letters to make up one of the capital cities highlighted, plus two rogue letters. By putting these rogue letters into the correct corresponding columns, it will be possible to reveal the capital city you should fly to for your next mission.

OKOMYTV	☐	☐
AHOYIRID	☐	☐
DRATJANKA	☐	☐
AGITATESON	☐	☐
JOKERVIAKEY	☐	☐

A spy has smuggled out the letters of a secret codeword by disguising them as graffiti painted on a wall visible to her contact.

Can you discover the six-letter word also, from this apparent mess of graffiti?

In order to discover the codeword, you must move through this maze. However, the enemy is not far behind, and should you attempt to re-use any letter you will surely get caught.

You have been told that the codeword is twelve letters long. Which route should you take?

You have a photograph to pass to your accomplice, but you do not know when you are supposed to meet her. However, when you next open your wallet you find that some lollipop sticks have been planted in there.

By rearranging and overlapping the sticks into a ladder shape, you find that the message reads...?

Which woman has left this cipher for you to decrypt?

CHOOSE
A
LETTER
FROM
EACH
LINE

Simply solve the code.

IWO EPE UST

NDE RSO ARR

RHO NTO ANG

WLO NOT EDI

NGI ICE NTH

TWI THA REE

LLT TTH VER

AKE ISM TIC

THE ESS ALC

AVE AGE OLU

RAG ISJ MNS

A typist for a rival organization is going on holiday. In order not to give her movements away, she has encoded them in a special way.

How many of her movements can you locate?

12th March: Tour of a European city
(6 letters using top row)

13th March: Visit a European capital city
(6 letters using left hand)

15th March: Tour of city in former Yugoslavia
(6 letters using left hand)

18th March: Arrive at famous U.S. city
(6 letters using middle row)

2nd April: Fly to South American capital
(7 letters using left hand)

10th April: 2 weeks holiday in U.S. resort
(8 letters using right hand)

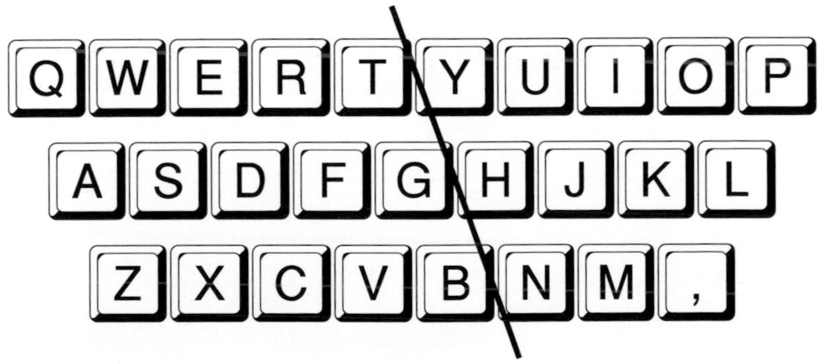

Someone at HQ has told you that you are urgently required to fly to a remote country, but they can't tell you which. They have said that you can find it out by following the paths in this maze, starting and finishing anywhere you like.

When you discover the intended answer, why might you think HQ are having a joke at your expense?

Use this CODE to find what you should wear at your next secret rendezvous.

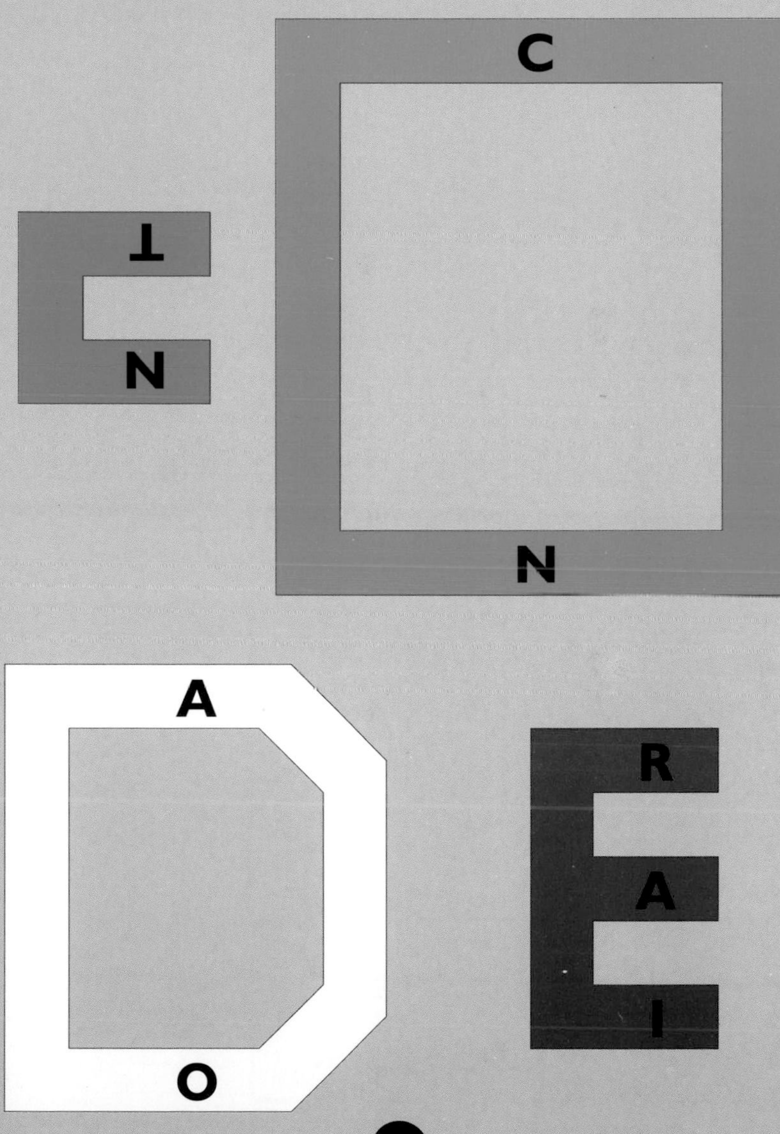

You have been provided with two similar, but not identical, pictures. By examining the picture in the grid against the one shown below right, deduce the six-letter codeword.

The six-letter codeword in this difficult puzzle is found by selecting the first letter from the top rectangle, the second from the next, and so on for each rectangle.

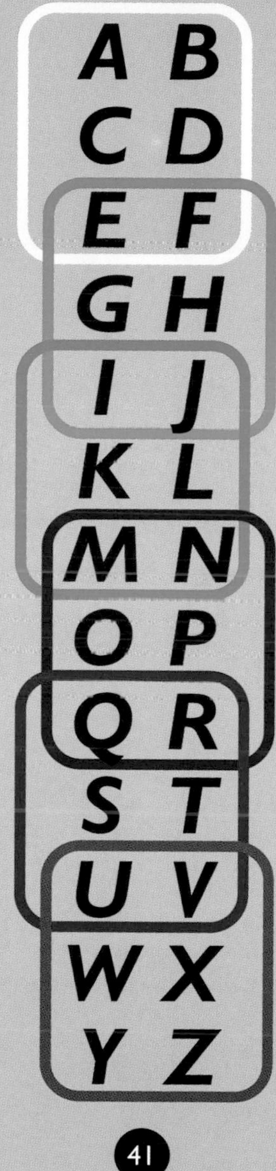

While on a mission in Europe, you are handed a parcel which contains the nine tiles illustrated. Rearrange them to find your next destination.

As an additional clue to start you off, every tile is either in the correct row *or* the correct column.

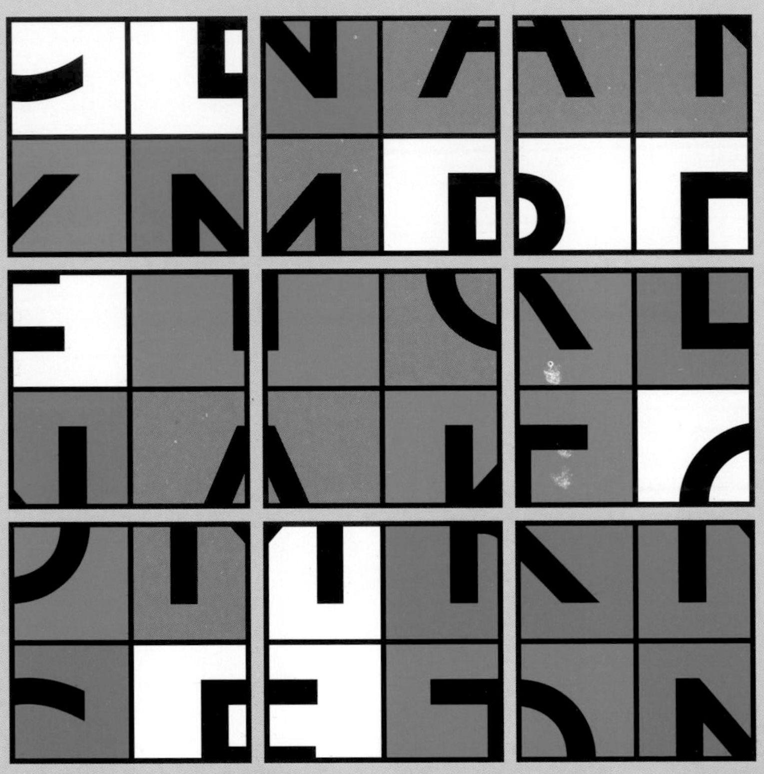

Your organization has managed to steal a secret formula from the enemy. Unfortunately, it appears to have been encoded. However, using your knowledge of chemistry, can you save the day and provide the complete solution?

1. Take equal parts of the three metals ✧✥✲✭✡✮☆✵✭, ✭✡✧✮✥✳☆✵✭ and ✭✡✮✧✡✮✥✳✥ and place them in a beaker of nitric acid. Xenon and argon (two of the ☼✌☼☜ ☝✌💧💧☜💧) will be given off.

2. When most of the liquid has evaporated, condense the residue.

3. The resulting ✲✥✳☆✮, when super-cooled, will provide enough energy equivalent to five thousand ✵✲✡✮☆✵✭ bombs.

A short message has been encrypted into the diagram shown below. Unfortunately, you have not been supplied with the key to crack the code.

Never the less,can you track down the message and then provide the answer to the question it poses?

You are a secret agent for the Government. Your directions have led you to a left luggage locker at the railway station. Your mission, should you decide to accept it, is to retrieve a microdot which has been hidden on an object.

When you open the locker, you find that there are six objects: an anorak, a model of a snowflake, eyeshadow, a toy canoe, a metronome and some banknotes. One of these objects is the correct one, and you must only take one object.

Can you work out how to complete your top secret mission?

If every counter is either on the correct row or on the correct column, how should the counters be rearranged?

Here, an amateur cryptologist (aged 2) has been busy at work setting a devious code using letter bricks.

Dismantle the pyramid brick-by-brick – you should find solving this is child's play.

You are at a locked door in a secret compound, and you have just 30 seconds to try to crack the lock before the guards return. Out comes the piece of glass you were given. This has been carved with the sequence required to open the four-digit combination lock. However, you don't know for sure which way up the perspex is supposed to go.

Each different combination takes 5 seconds to enter into the keypad. Will you be certain of making it in time?

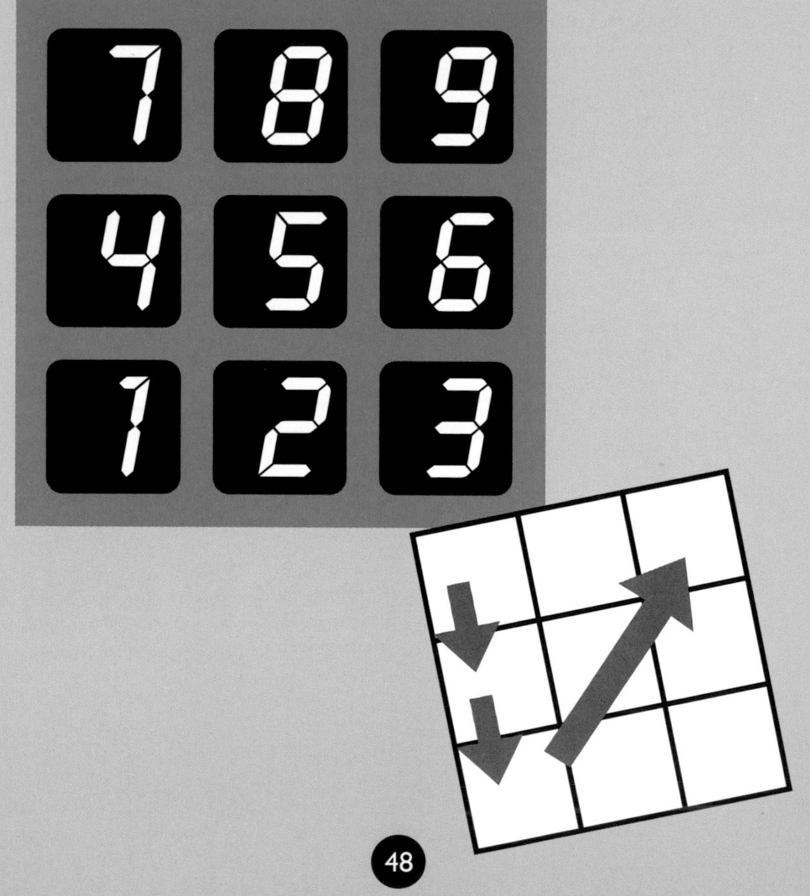

Answer the clues, then enter them into the grid. The nine letters can be rearranged to find the surname of the next secret agent you must contact.

YELLOW	*Custom*
GREEN	*Number*
BLUE	*Existed*
RED	*Superlative*

Here are five different shapes with their associated numbers. How many different numbers can the rectangle represent?

Circle = 50

Cylinder = 5

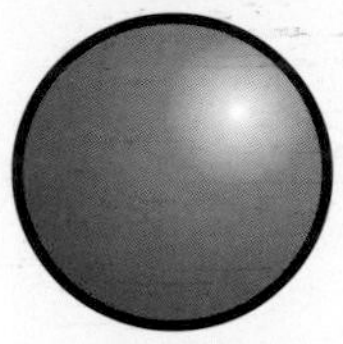

Sphere = 1 or 3

Ring = 7 or 8

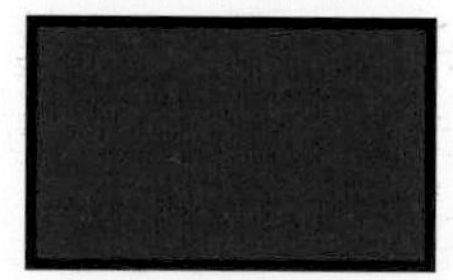

Rectangle = ?

This shopping list for food and other various household items was found in the handbag of an enemy agent.

However, a little bit of re-arranging will show you that this list isn't as innocent as it first seems. Why?

EGGS

PEARS

PLUGS

WAFFLE

ONIONS

CAMPARI

PETIT POIS

GRENADINE

A simple, three-button code sequence must be punched into the keypad in exactly the right order, otherwise the bomb will go off.

Using the instructions from the bomb defusing manual, can you save the day?

Instructions

1. *If the red button is pressed first, the yellow is second.*

2. *If the red button is pressed second, the yellow is third.*

3. *If the yellow button is not pressed first, the blue is second.*

4. *No button is pressed more than once.*

5. *Do not hit the bomb with a large mallet.*

You have been instructed to investigate the murder of renowned cryptologist Dr. X. The field of suspects has already been narrowed down to four of his rivals: Celia Krypto, Thomas Morse, Danielle Coad and Sam O'Fore.

"How was the body found?" you inquire. The detective investigating the case explains: "He was stabbed from behind while sat at his bureau. There was nothing nearby except for a telephone. Here's the list of phone numbers."

He hands you a copy of the telephone bill. All the numbers appear to be local take-away restaurants, except the final one – (0213) 715 8539.

Who would you interrogate first?

Revolve the concentric tumblers on this safe in order to spell out a six-letter word.

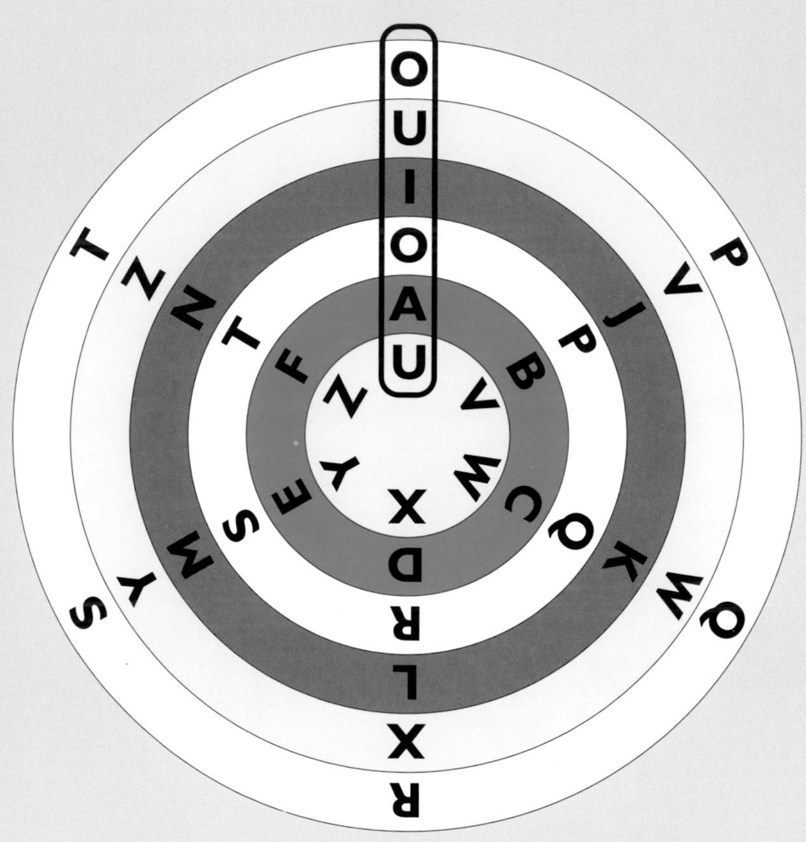

The four-letter codeword required is **not** illustrated here. However, the five pictures here should give you a very good clue as to what the answer is.

This is a cryptogram, where each symbol represents a different letter of the alphabet. Because letters are used in different frequencies in written language, it is usually possible to work out the code.

Armed with this information, can you decipher the following message?

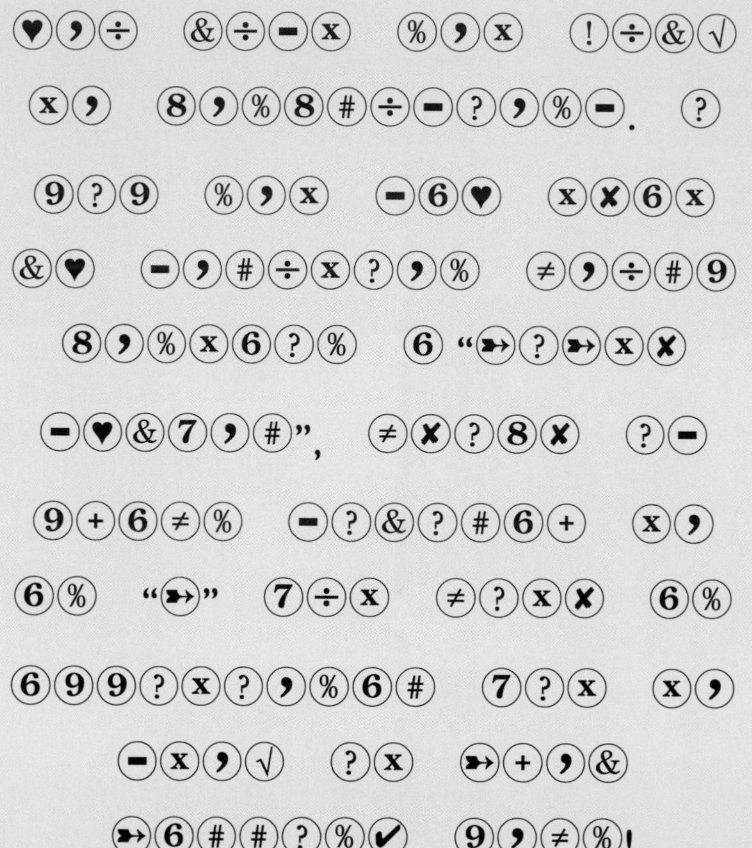

Follow this numerical maze to find a four-digit code number. UK readers will find a significance in their final answer, and international readers should add 934 to their total to find a different solution which is arguably more significant.

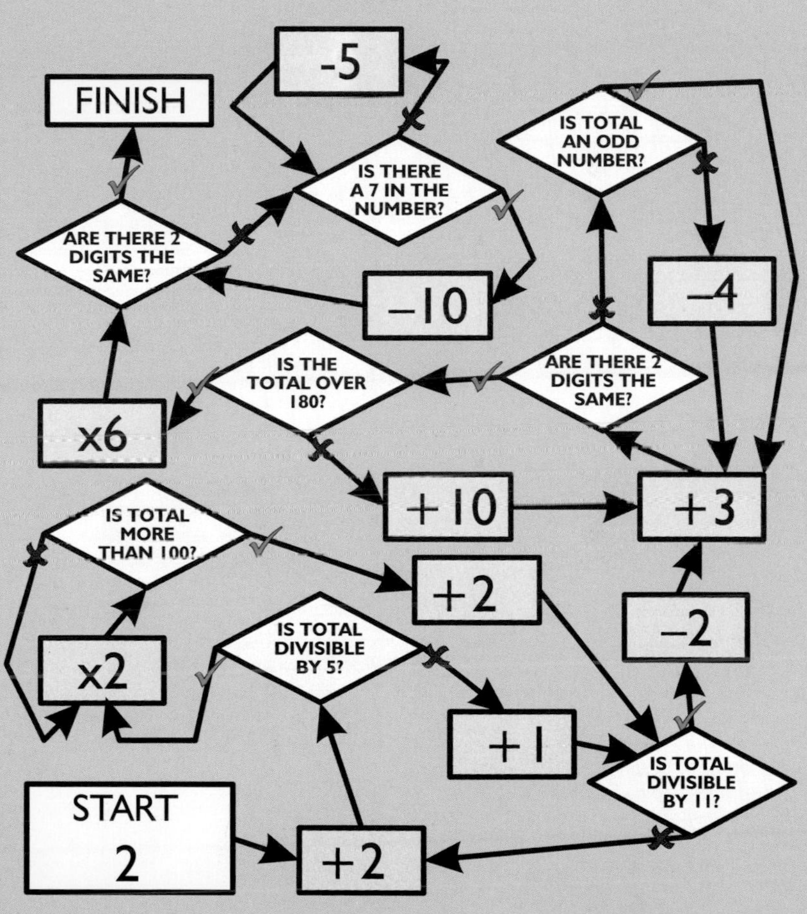

Move each letter tile one square horizontally or vertically *exactly* five times, avoiding the blocked squares as you do so.

What coded message then lies within one of the columns?

Reassembling these cut-out pieces will provide an eight-letter codeword.

Using the usual chess moves for a knight, king and bishop, land on the squares that spell out appropriate words. Each word is at least eight letters long.

In a test to see whether you are an imposter, you are presented with a list of words inside a box. Only one of the words outside the box logically belongs inside the box also. When you work out the logic, you will also find out your call signal for the assignment.

VENOMOUS SHOWTIME AXIS MENINGITIS ?	CORONET MARZIPAN RHYTHM IGLOO FIRESIDE FLUFFY

What letter of the English alphabet should replace the question mark?

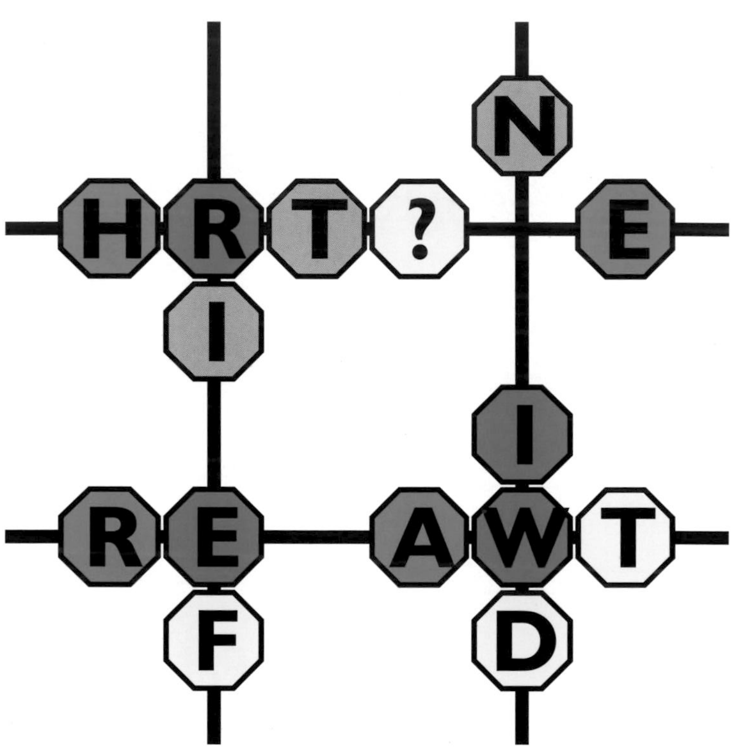

In Britain, car registration plates are of the format: one letter, followed by a number between 1 and 999, followed by three more letters.

The Special Branch police force have penetrated the communication networks of a terrorist organization. They suspect that messages are being passed in newspaper advertisements for buying and selling registration plates.

An informant has told you that LIE LOW appeared in the adverts shown on the right.

Using this lead, can you decode the message represented on the left?

G 1 THG
N 3 IRS
A 8 RET
B 17 TEL
H 13 DAE
J 4 RTU
R 1 BER
Y 2 EHS
P 16 EUL
E 26 CON

F 6 ERO
D 5 MTI
X 7 GID
A 11 DNA
E 10 RET
C 20 TEL

What symbol should replace the question mark in this sequence?

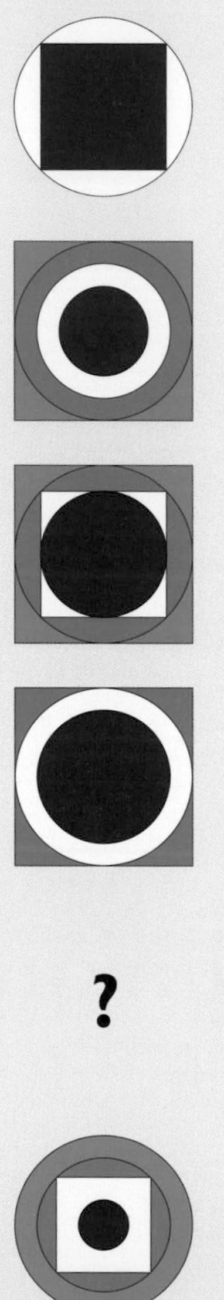

The entry to the back door of an enemy surveillance post is opened by standing on a series of pressure pans in the floor, as illustrated.

The only clue you have been given as to how to open the door is a piece of paper which reads:

STEP PETS PETS

Given that you begin on the "E" as illustrated, what word will open the door and allow you to progress with your secret mission?

Can you solve this arrow-based puzzle?

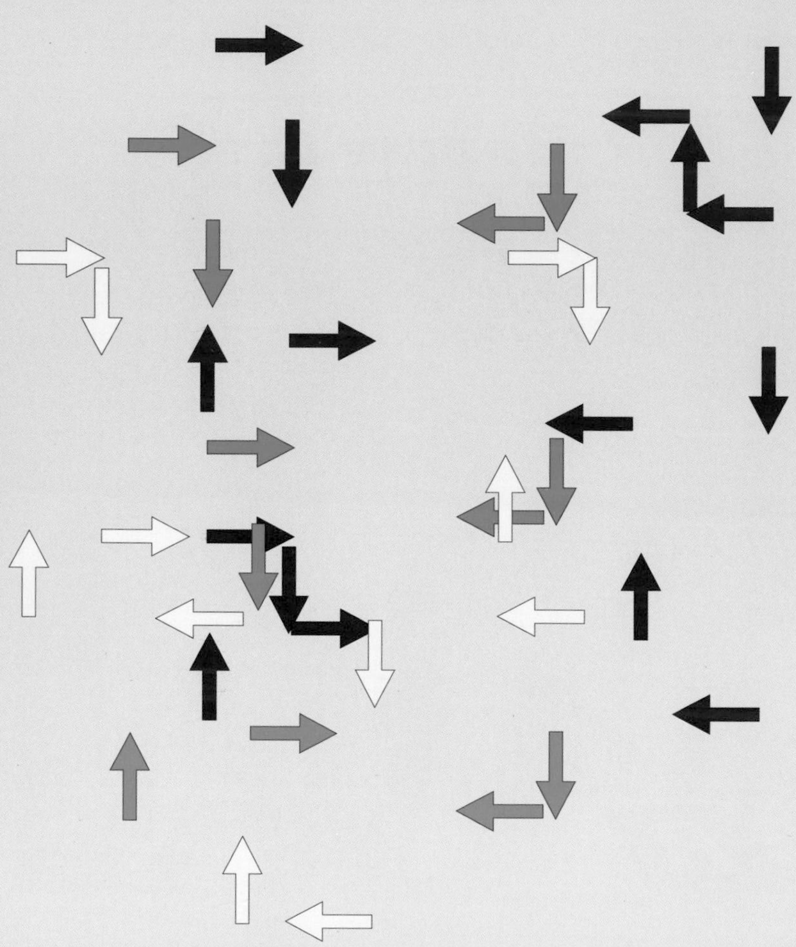

In this game, your aim is to find a seven-letter codeword. Before you do this, you must first work out what the seven letters are.

Try to decipher what the six clues are trying to tell you, and then enter one letter into each segment of the main diagram.

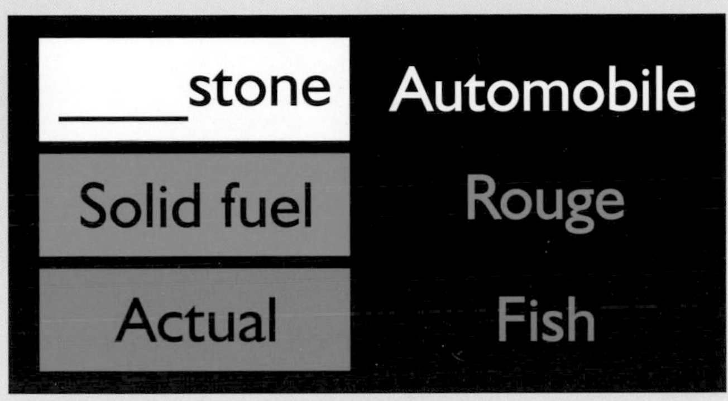

A two part challenge – decode the anagrams and place them into the **appropriate** lines on the grid.

Then see how many six-letter words you can form by choosing one word from each line, starting from the top and moving down one line each time.

CAUSE
LATER
CAMGI
VEERF
USHOE
REBAD

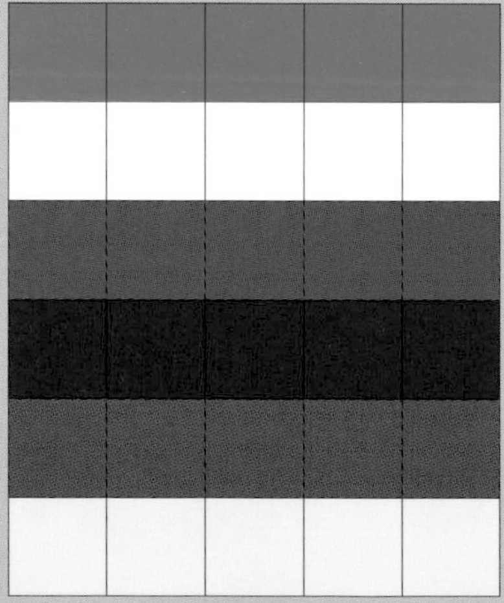

These codewords have been hidden beneath some railway tracks so that only alternate letters can be seen. Can you decipher them?

Clues (in no particular order) are:
Fight, Word book, Polygon, Animal, Time limit.

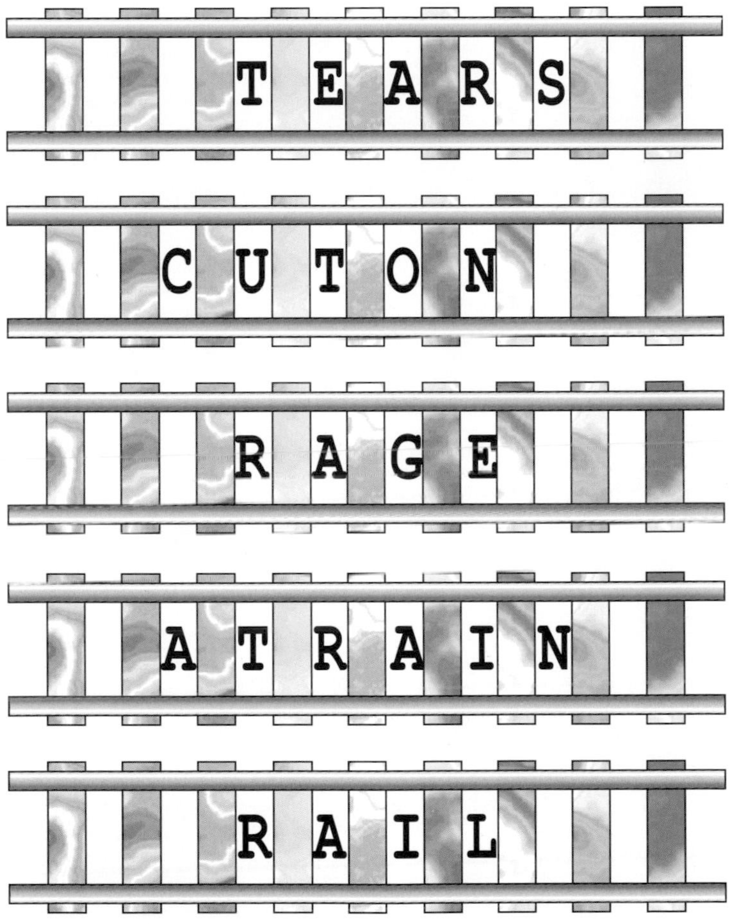

Jane picked up a strange piece of paper from the floor. It looked like something secret. On one side it had *"D. H. Lawrence, Judy Garland and a trout"*. The other side is illustrated below.

Can you work out what the message says?

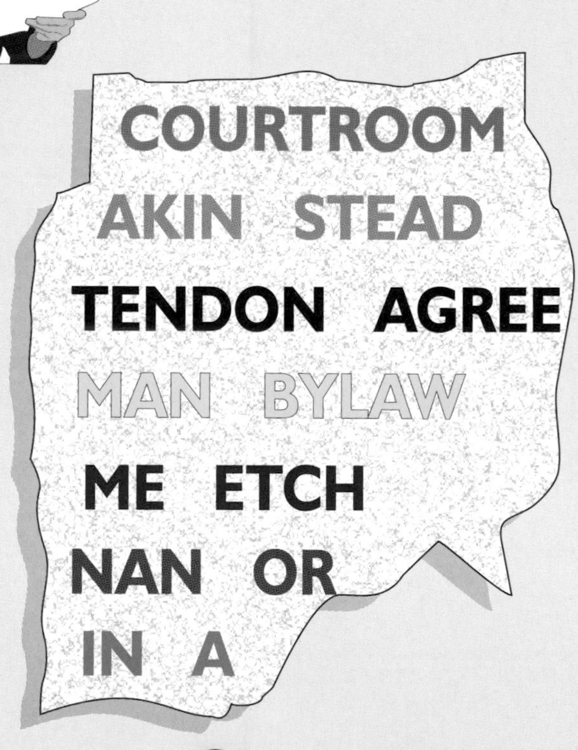

In most of these puzzles, there is often a clue in the question. However, this puzzle takes things one step further.

What extremely useful piece of information does this coded question ask of you?

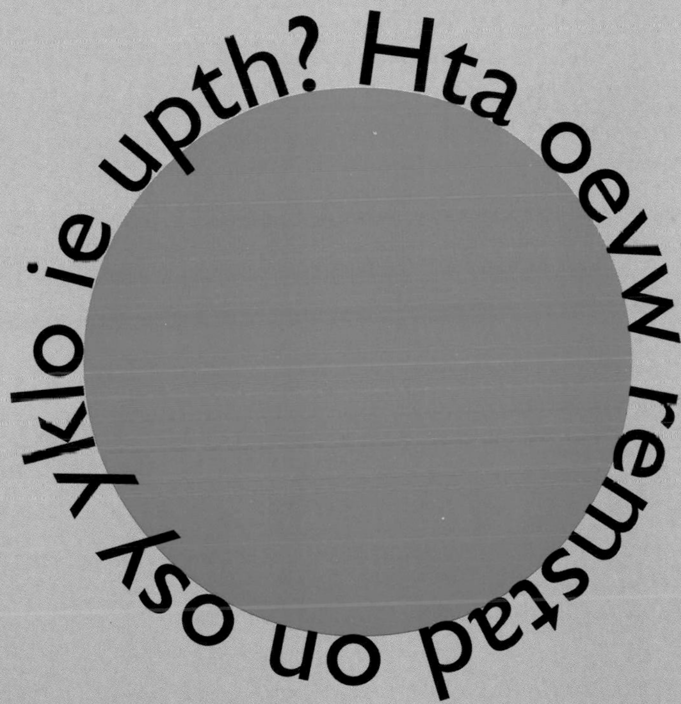

Some of the letters on this keyboard have been eliminated already. To eliminate some more, answer the general knowledge questions about mathematics. You can eliminate the first letter of your answers from the keyboard.

When you have finished, only eight keys should remain. What eight-letter word can be typed using each key once?

1) Type of tables invented by John Napier, opposite of the exponential (9)
2) The numbers 1, 2, 3, 6, 8 and 12 are all ________ of 24 (7)
3) Half the diameter of a circle (6)
4) In calculus, the reverse operation of integration (15)
5) Fraction with a "1" as the numerator and a "4" as the denominator (7)
6) Number system with base two, uses only 0s and 1s (6)
7) Array of numbers, usually written between brackets (6)
8) Numbers such as 0, 1, 2, 3, ... etc. (5)
9) Archimedes found this measure of a circle to be 2πr (13)

PASSWORD : ☐☐☐☐☐☐☐☐

Another day, another bomb to diffuse.

However, this time we can't help you out so much. You see, I know that, of the clues provided, at least one of them is true. However, I also know for sure that at least one of the clues is a red herring put in there by the enemy to disturb any potential bomb crackers.

Cutting the correct wire will disarm the bomb and prevent it from being used – which one is it to be?

Your aim is to obtain a particular eight-digit code number. This code number only contains the digits 1 to 4, but you know nothing more than that.

However, you have been told how to find the number. Start with a "1". On the next line, describe how many 1s, 2s, 3s and 4s there are (i.e. one "1"). This is your next line. Then continue (i.e. two "1"s) etc.

The boffins say that, if you continue the sequence far enough, the correct solution will become obvious eventually because it is the last number in the series.

What is the eight-digit code required?

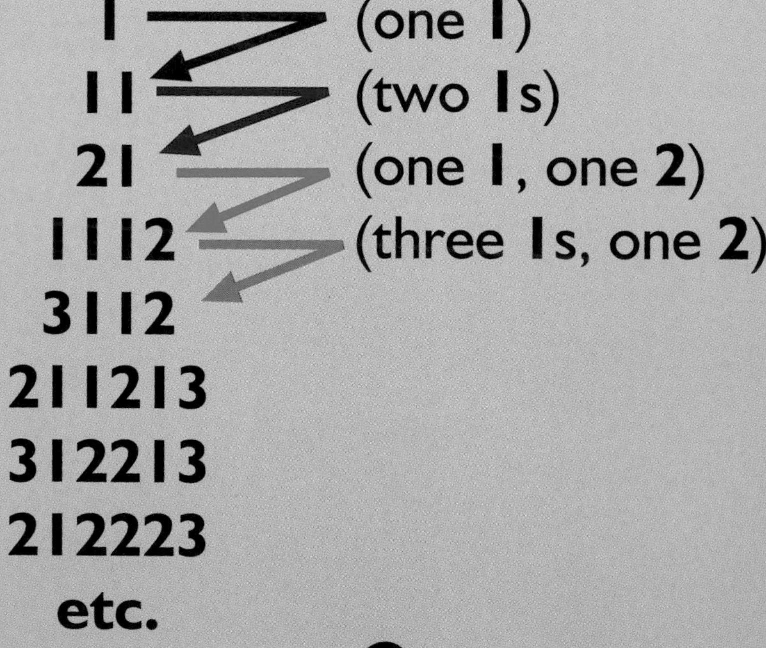

You're on surveillance duty late one evening to ensure the safety of Mrs. Clare Todd, the wife of the press baron who is taking part in a conference this evening.

You are biding your time by doing the crossword but, being the expert puzzle-solver you are, it's not long before that's polished off.

Then you suddenly become extremely alarmed and begin to make plans for how you're going to get Mrs. Todd out of there, and fast.

What message did you read?

In this puzzle, there are at least two codewords you could possibly find by moving the columns up and down, and reading across the red stripe indicated.

Find either word.

You are given a test by another agent who wants to test your cryptology ability.

Given that the items shown below are acceptable, you must name another item which could also be acceptable.

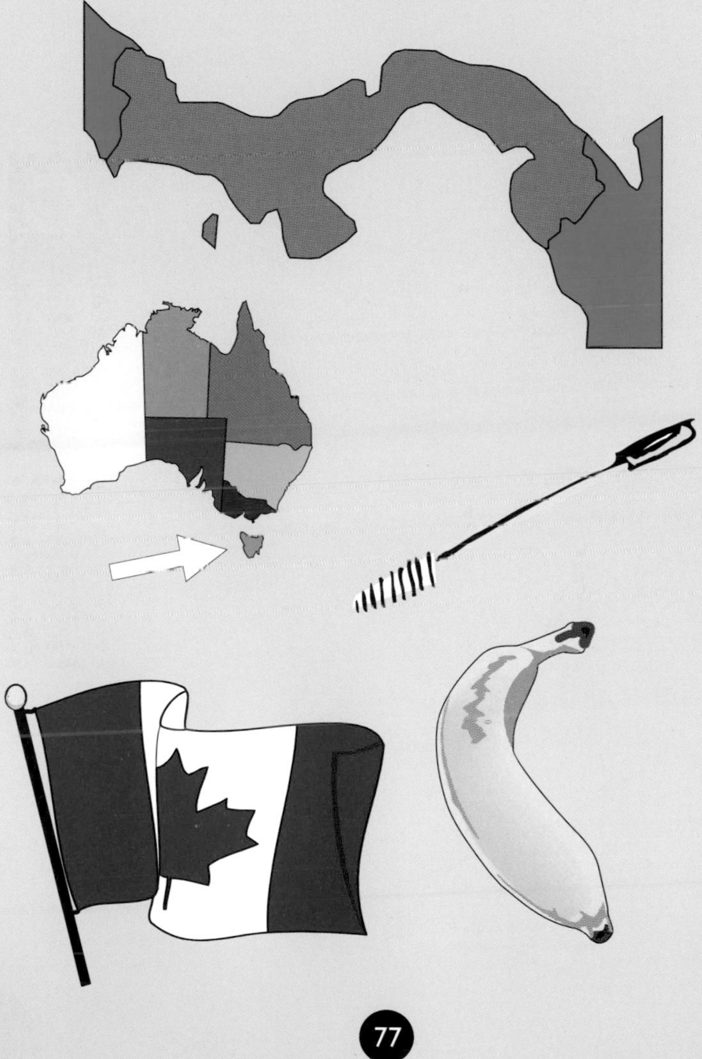

Given that the ball always bounces the same vertical distance each time, care to guess what word will be formed on the ball's travels?

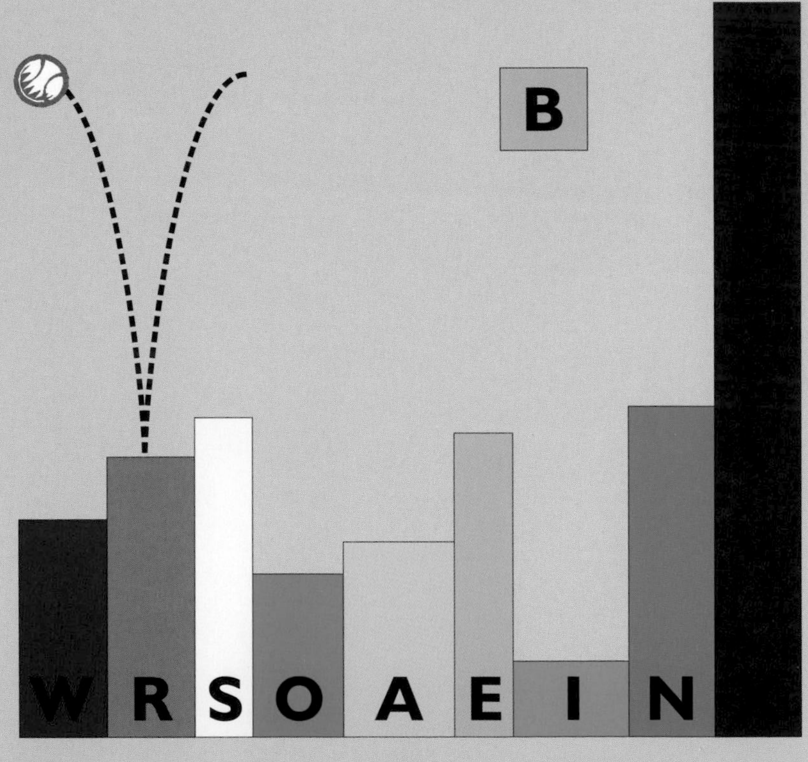

Crack this code by looking for something that isn't there.

PAR	LEY
RAM	KIN
FORE	LOSE
TANG	AM
FIR	TRAP
LO	US

You are trying to find the eight-letter password to enter the enemy base. However, you seem to be having trouble deciphering it.

Any ideas what it is?

Crack the safe by deciding whether the statements below are true or false. This will lead to the correct two-digit code number.

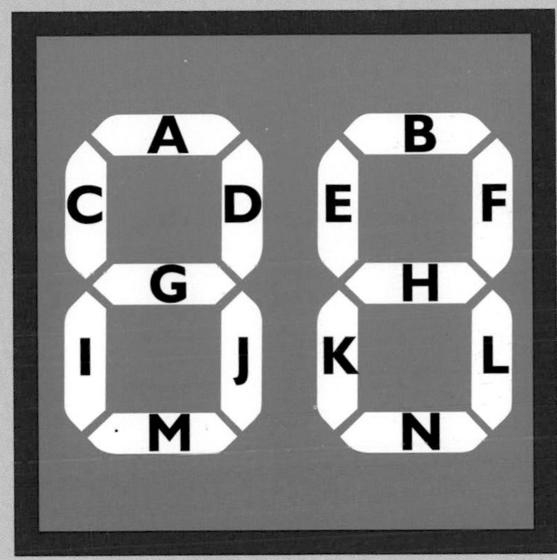

A) The novel "A Tale of Two Cities" is set in London and Paris
B) The flag of Iran is a plain green rectangle
C) The decimal version of π has an infinite number of digits
D) "Je Ne Sais Quoi" is French for "I don't know what"
E) Ananas comusus is the Latin name for the banana
F) Iolanthe is a Gilbert and Sullivan operetta
G) Poseidon was the Greek God of the Sea
H) Roy Rogers' horse was called Scout
I) Albert Polaroid invented the first film camera
J) Bix Beiderbecke played the cornet
K) Calvados is a liqueur made from almonds
L) A euphemism is a way of expressing something more nicely
M) I is not a prime number
N) Henry V was a member of the House of Orange

This message hasn't been encrypted at all, although it has been obscured rather.

Can you see through the clutter and work out what you have to do?

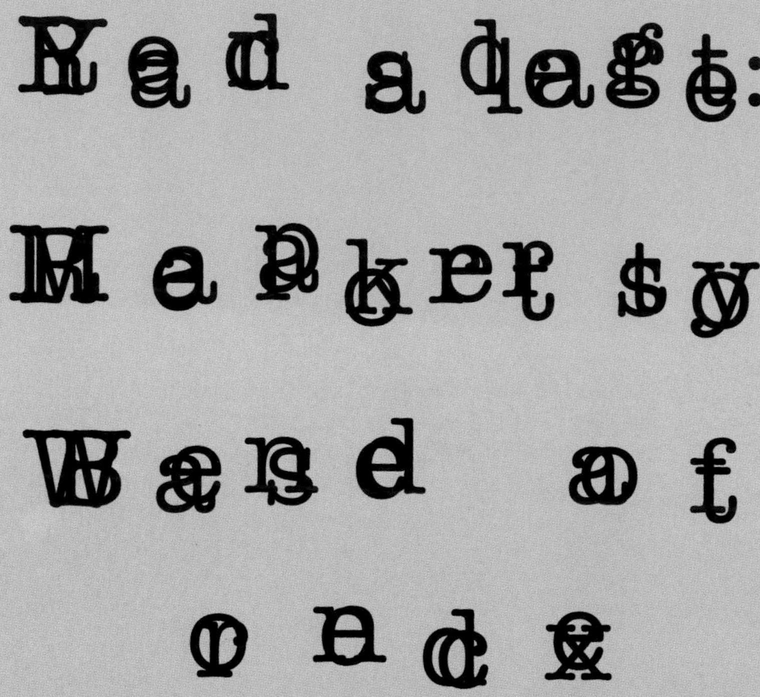

In this code, your aim is to eliminate five sets of related letters, so that you are left with some seemingly random letters. These remaining letters will form a five-letter codeword.

Start eliminating.

S

B

P O

T

E S

L A I

U

C D E

A O

N

L P U T E

H

R

I L

E

S D

T

E

By using each path once only, find the 14-letter codeword.

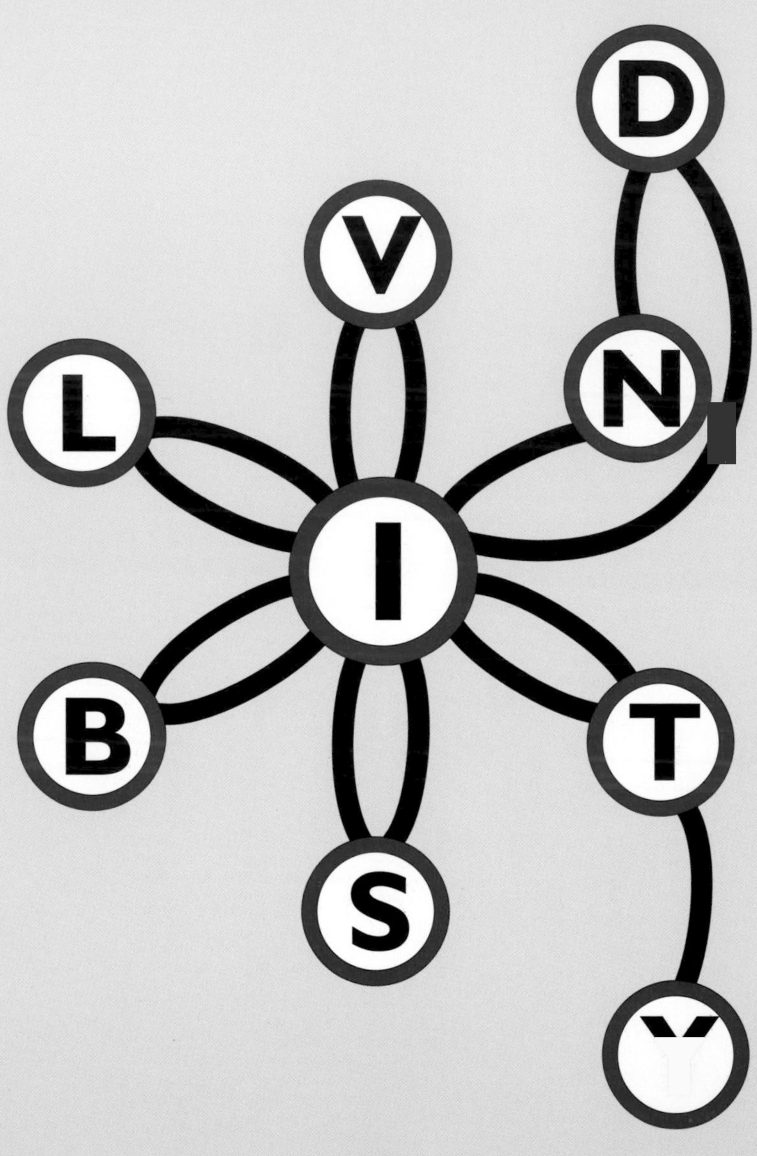

This looks very similar to a code you've encountered previously in this book. However, unfortunately it is a different code.

This time, your aim is to find a six-letter codeword.

Tracing a route between facing bricks, what is the most *appropriate* six-letter word that can be found here?

You've been informed that it's possible to trace a ten-letter codeword, with the letters in the correct order, by passing through this maze without ever crossing your path or using any part of the maze twice. Many people have tried it, but failed.

Can you triumph over the labyrinth?

Which of my felt-tip pens should I use to shade in the H?

K N K

E D E

N Y H

This looks like someone has jammed the keys on their typewriter. However, look closer and you should be able to detect a coded message in there somewhere.

MEMATEUATN

ETETHHTTE

I have a monster that lives in my basement, and we use a primitive code to communicate.

For example, if it says the number "16", I know it wants a vegetable to eat. If it says the number "10", I know it wants to eat a bird, and a grunt of "2" means it fancies a nice juicy insect. "20" means it's thirsty.

What should I do if, one day, it says "21"?

Complete with words. What can you locate down column shown?

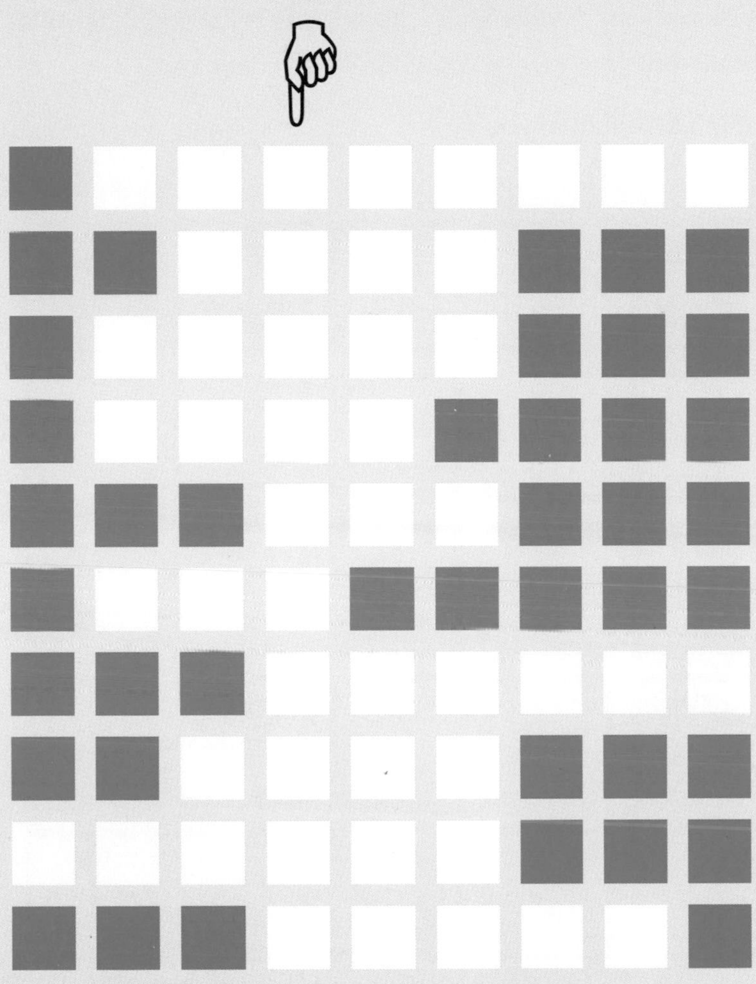

You must open the correct box marked with a star. However, only one box is correct, and the others are booby traps.

Start with the middle box. The answer is “abrupt”. So that should tell you how to move on to the next box.

Which box should you open?

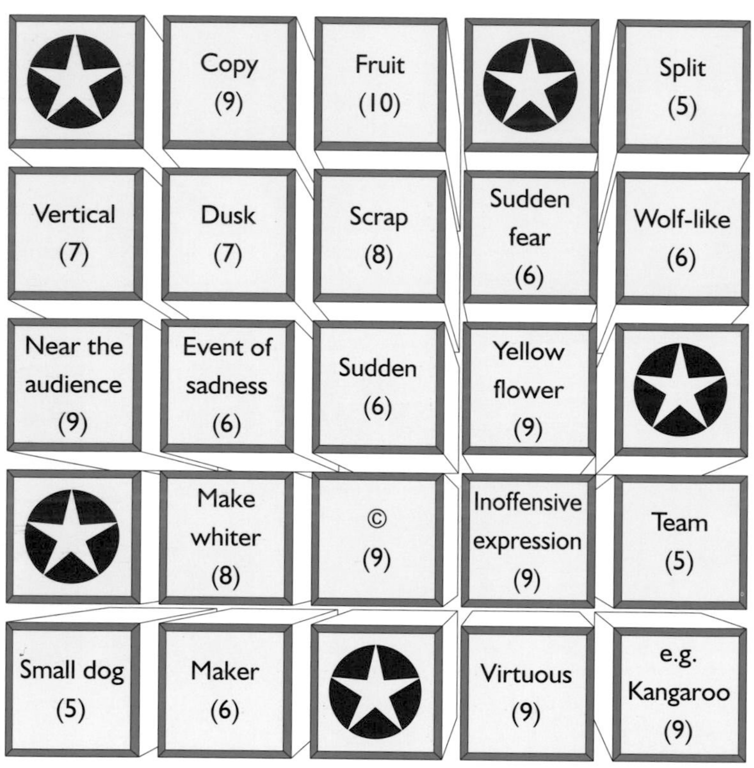

A spy has been using a typewriter cipher to create codewords for contacting other agents on her secret missions.

We have managed to find out the words used on her previous missions. We also know the next word is going to be eight letters long.

Can you detect a pattern, and thus predict what the codeword for Mission 8 is going to be?

Mission 1: ACCESSED
Mission 2: DEFERRERS
Mission 3: REGRETTED
Mission 4: FRY
Mission 5: HUMBUG
Mission 6: MINIMUM
Mission 7: MUKLUK
Mission 8: ????????

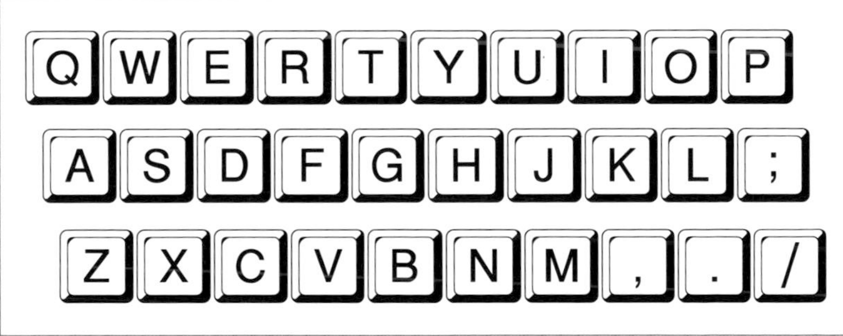

Rotate the code wheels so that a word is formed in the red loop.

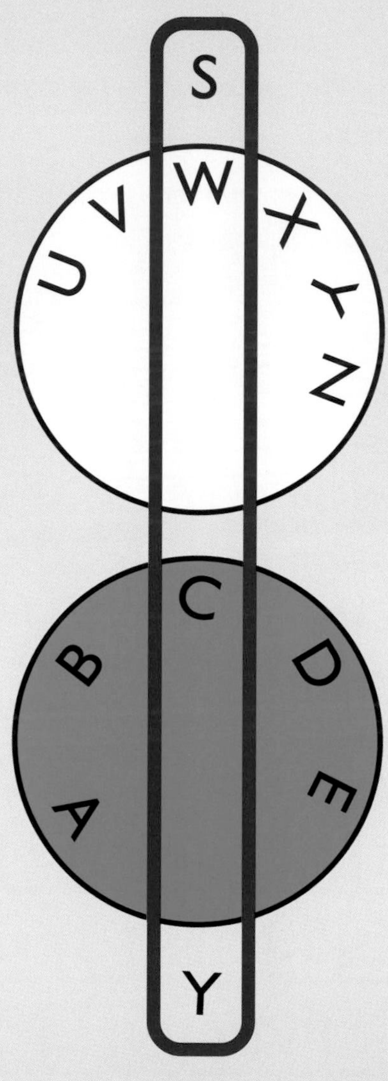

The boffins at the lab have been trying to work out what this strange sequence of lines is. They think it might be a bar code of some description, but I think it's something a lot simpler.

What do you think the bars are representing?

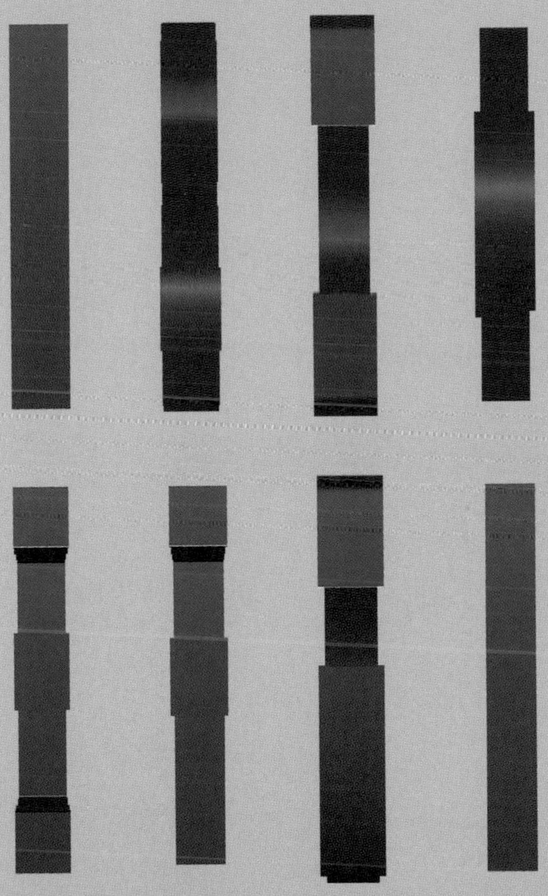

Solve these clues, which are in alphabetical order. The first letters of each answer are an anagram of the eight-letter codeword required.

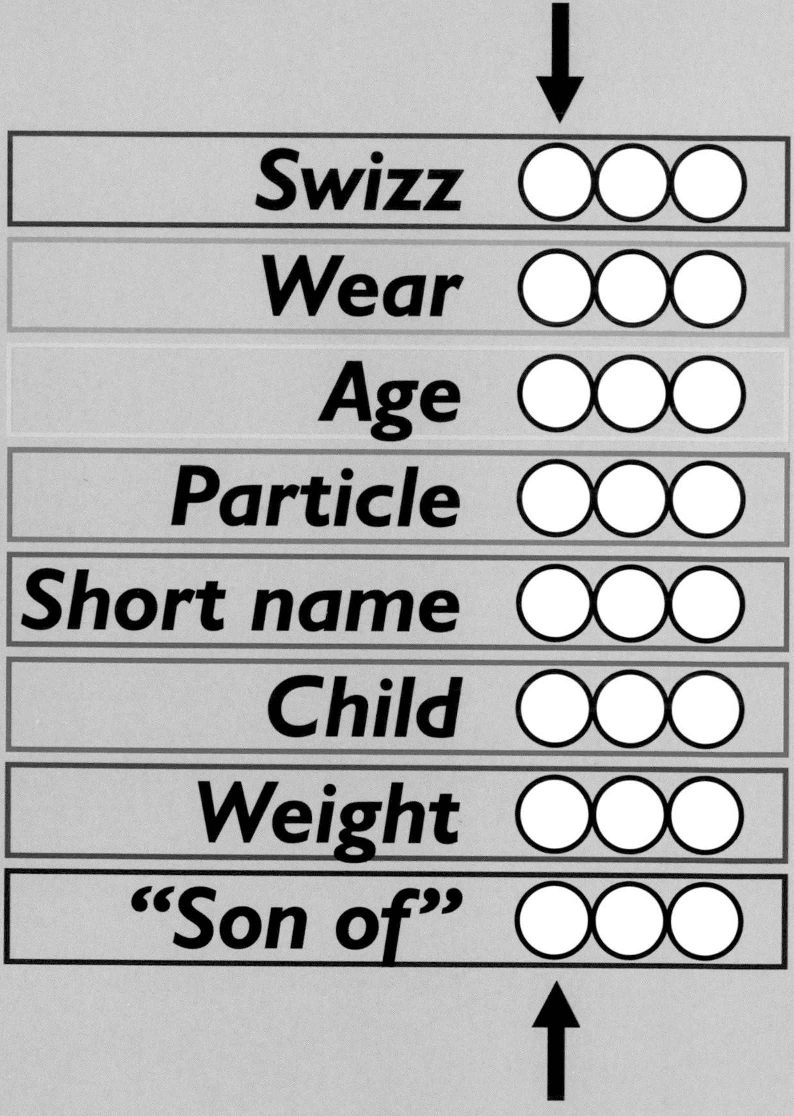

I'm out in the main street of the city, trying to punch in my secret code into the number lock to enter my lab. I've been told to push the button that's above the red star, below the white X, to the right of the blue circle, and to the left of the green square. However, I can't find the button anywhere!

Can you see where I'm going wrong? And which button should I be pressing?

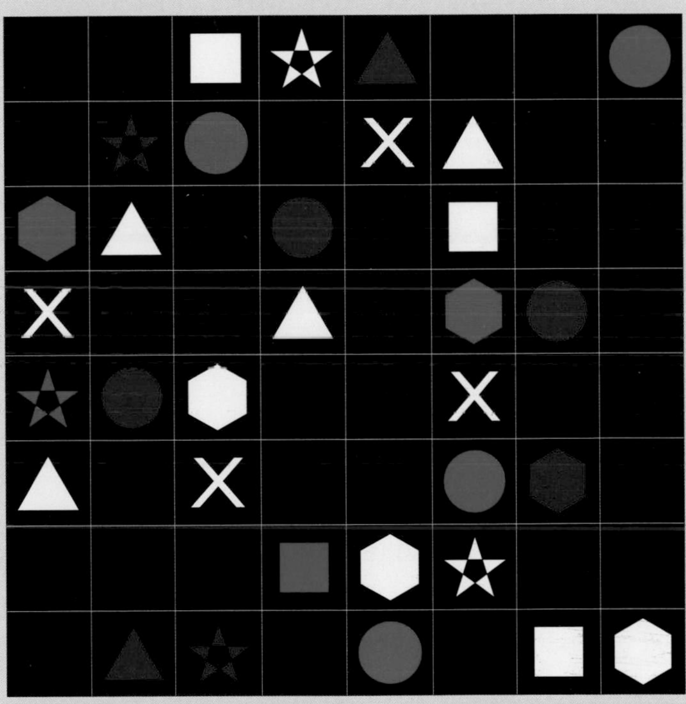

Can you crack this off-beat code?

1 is a surprise

2 starts to say something

3 depends on where you are

4 is rich

5 takes its share

6 is pointy

7 is a connector

8 is a touch of Hollywood

9 has a bulge in the middle

Find the nine-letter codeword. Not all the letters or arrows are used.

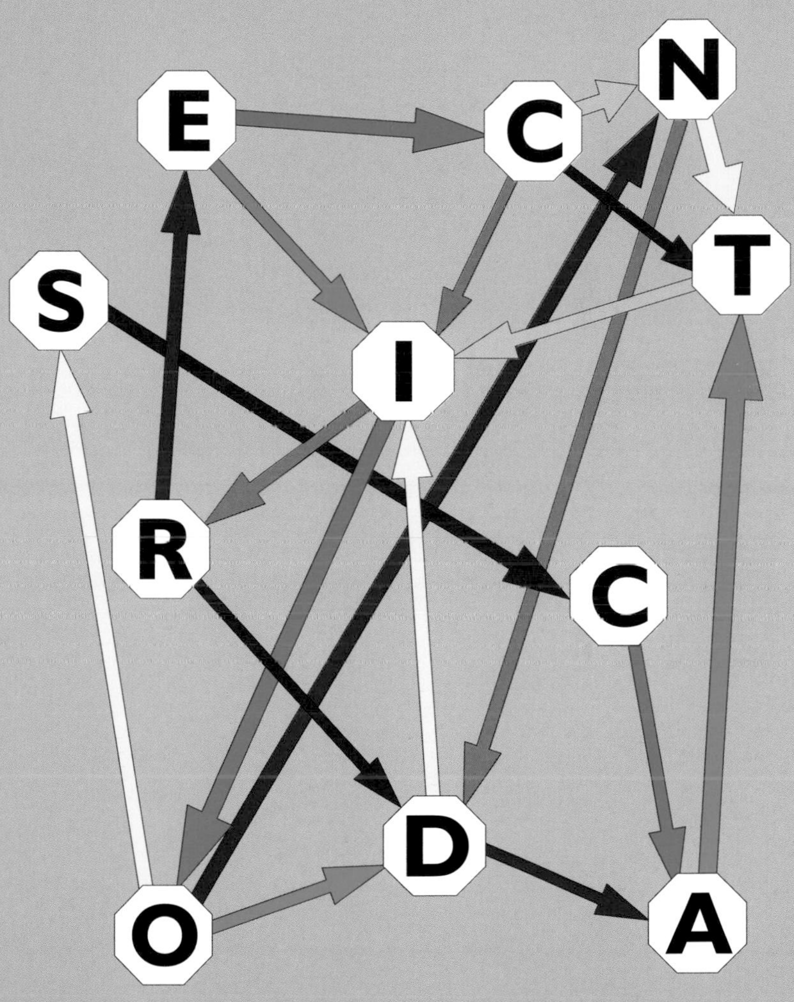

Someone's tried to censor this message, but there's just enough left showing for you to try and work it out.

What does it say?

ANSWERS

ANSWERS TO PUZZLES ENDING IN –1

1 The map shows that the bird stopped at California, Utah, Colorado, Kansas, Oklahoma, Ohio – the first letters of which spell cuckoo.

11 When the spiral picture is assembled, the message reads across each row SAYY OUKN OWAN DREW, which (when respaced) gives SAY YOU KNOW ANDREW.

21 There is one line missing from each letter, then the whole thing has been reflected left-to-right. The original word reads ADVANTAGE.

31 The capitals are TOKYO, RIYADH, JAKARTA, SANTIAGO and REYKJAVIK. The spare letters, reading down the columns, should give MONTEVIDEO.

41 The only words we could find are BIJOUX and CHINTZ.

51 The shopping list becomes less innocent if you overlap the correct two items and then examine the red parts. For example, the red parts of CAMPARI and TRIFLE give RIFLE:

CAMPARIFLE

Similarly for PETIT POIS and ONIONS (POISON), GRENADINE and EGGS (GRENADE) and PLUGS and PEARS (SPEAR).

61 Coronet is the missing word. As the question tries to imply, there is something significant about reading the words backwards. Each word in the box contains a number when reversed (suomoneV etc.) Your call sign is therefore One-Two-Six-Nine-Ten.

71 Jump three letters each time round the circle. The question you reveal asks you "How many letters do you have to skip", which isn't a very useful clue given that you'd already worked out the answer by then!

81 The combination is 91. Shade out the segments relating to false statements to see why. A) TRUE, B) FALSE (that is Libya's flag), C) TRUE, D) TRUE, E) FALSE (it is the pineapple), F) TRUE, G) TRUE, H) FALSE (it was called Trigger), I) FALSE (it was Fox Talbot), J) TRUE, K) FALSE (made from apples), L) TRUE, M) TRUE, N) FALSE (he was in the House of Plantagenets).

91 Did you solve this puzzle. If so, it's MIRACULOUS!

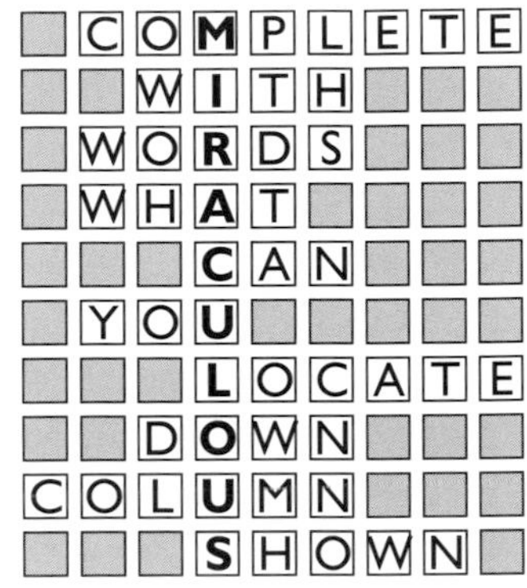

ANSWERS TO PUZZLES ENDING IN –2

2 The squares must contain **GIOOTTUY** and a blank. Clue 1: the **O** must be in the central square. Clue 2: **OOT** must be the middle row. Clue 3: As they are the only vowels left to place, the **I** and **U** must appear in the top-right and bottom-left squares in some order. Clue 4: the **Y** and **G** must appear top-left and top-middle. Remaining blank must be at the bottom right. With a little trial and error thereafter, you should have obtained the message **YOU GOT IT,** reading down each column.

12 If 5 is first, look at line 5, which is like a ransom note, so go to line 4 next. Line 4 says "Ransom Note" in Greek letters, so we go to line 7. Continuing, the full code is 54731628.

22 The dangerous atom is C. The other eleven letters, going from bond to bond, spell out SWITZERLAND, a neutral country.

32 If you look very carefully, you will find that the letters of the word QUARTZ are on the wall.

42 It looks like you're off to Italy, to see Mount ETNA:

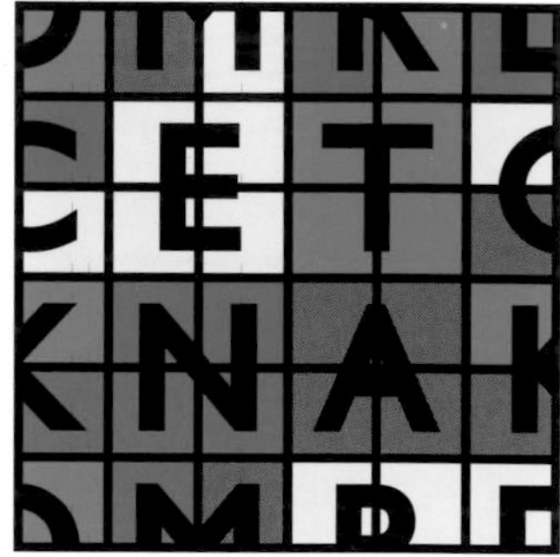

52 The only combination that works is Yellow then Blue then Red.

62 It should be a letter "A", so that the four skewers contain the letters for the four basic elements: EARTH, WIND, FIRE and WATER.

72 The answers are:

1) Logarithm, 2) Factors, 3) Radius, 4) Differentiation, 5) Quarter, 6) Binary, 7) Matrix, 8) Whole, 9) Circumference. Eliminating the first letters of each answer leaves the word HEPTAGON.

82 The message says RED ALERT: REPORT TO BASE AT ONCE.

92 All the answers contain the letters "up", "down", "left" or "right". The correct route is abr**up**t, **left**over, sun**down**, **down**er, b**right**en, copy**right**, e**up**hemism, butterc**up**, f**right**, l**up**ine and c**left**, leading you to the star near the top-right corner.

ANSWERS TO PUZZLES ENDING IN –3

3 Connect the dots as shown and read the answer in the direction of the arrow.

13 Each tick represents a number, which in turn represents a letter. For example, the top tick in the grid is in box 3, which corresponds to the letter I. Therefore, the answer is EXECUTION.

23 The machine will eventually crank out the word PIRATES.

33 The word you're looking for is AMBIDEXTROUS.

43 The missing words are: Germanium, Magnesium, Manganese, Rare gasses, Resin, Uranium. Each symbol in the question represented a different letter of the alphabet.

53 Thomas Morse is a key suspect: it looks like the victim might have pressed the buttons for (0213) to draw the "T", then pressed 7158539 to draw the "M". Of course, someone could have done this after the murder to frame Morse instead.

63 The plates read HQ IS UNSAFE. Take the year letter given, and advance the given number of letters along from there. The groups of three letters backwards read... well, see for yourself!

73 You should cut the green wire – this way the two statements pertaining to the blue wire are true, and the red wire statement is false. Cutting the red would give three "true"s, and the blue would give three "falses"

.83 You can draw straight lines through equidistant letters for LOCUST, BEETLE, ANT, SPIDER and APHID. The remaining letters make up the word LOUSE.

93 See diagram below. Each mission uses letters from an area of nine letters on the keyboard.

After each mission, the trapezium is moved one space to the right. For mission 8, the only eight-letter word that can be formed from IOPKL is LOLLIPOP.

ANSWERS TO PUZZLES ENDING IN –4

4 The number of sides on each shape represents the number of "clicks" you can turn the dial, and the circle represents 0 (i.e. no more moves). Start with 6-sided shape as shown. Turn 6 clicks counter-clockwise (to triangle), 3 clockwise (to prism), then 5 counter-clockwise (to circle).

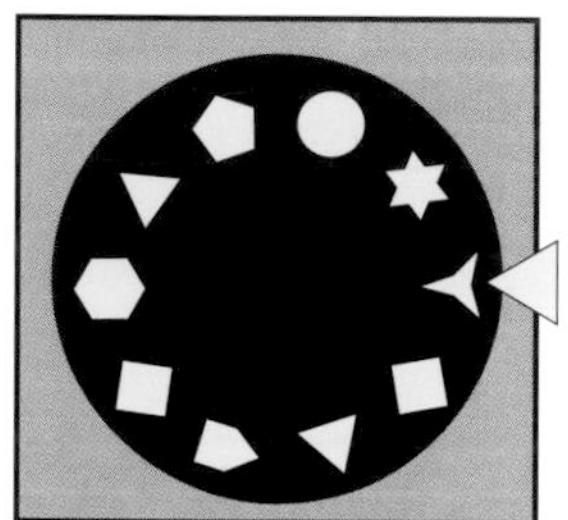

14 Turning right at every circle, and turning left at every diamond, gives: MEET ME AT STATUE IN THE MARKET SQUARE FOR TEA.

24 Precede each word with a letter to make the words five letters long. These letters spell A SIMPLE MESSAGE when read from bottom to top:

34 Overlapping the rungs with the main poles gives the message BRING ME PHOTO AT SEVEN PM:

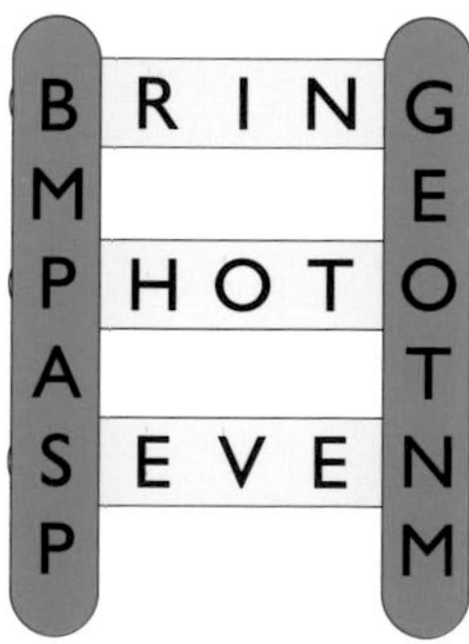

44 By cycling through yellow, blue, green and orange, you obtain the message WHAT IS THE MIDDLE LETTER? The middle letter on the diagram is the central “X”.

54 The only word that you can find is SYNTAX.

64 A large, red dot to represent the letter “E”. The symbols represent successive letters of the alphabet expressed in Morse code. Circles represent dots, squares represent dashes, all arranged in order of outside first, inside last.

74 If you keep the series going long enough, you get to the number 21322314. If you write out the description of that, you get “two 1s, three 2s, two 3s and one 4” – in other words, it generates itself and so must be the last term in the series.

84 The word is INDIVISIBILITY.

94 The word is SUNDAY.

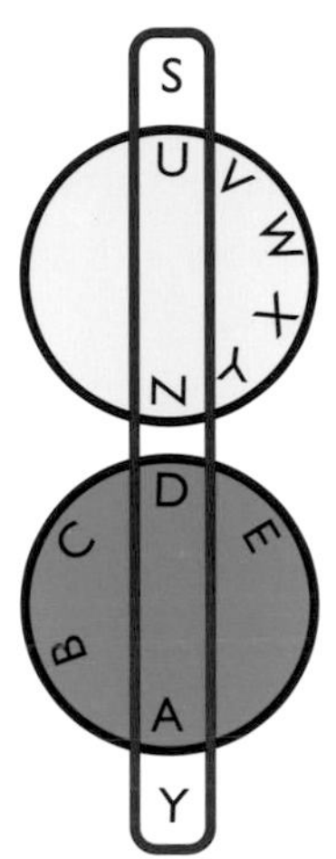

ANSWERS TO PUZZLES ENDING IN –5

5 By thinking about the segments that aren't lit, you can see your attire should be black **tie**...

15 The spaces are all filled in by the names of cities: "...by air OR LAND Or sea", "do your WASHING TONight", "lots of hoBOS TONight", "known as anarCHIC AGOraphobics", "is a sandWICH ITAlians like to eat", "you must hELP A SOn" (El Paso).

25 You should have crossed out E, M, S, P, T and I which gives the word CRAYON.

35 CARMEL has, because her name can be spelled out if you do what the question says.

45 You should choose the eyeshadow. The word e**yes**hadow contains YES, whereas bank**no**tes, a**no**rak, s**no**wflake, ca**no**e and metro**no**me all contain NO.

55 The final word is OPTS. The pictures represent five anagrams of this word: POST, STOP, TOPS, SPOT, and POTS.

65 The piece of paper is a rebus which represents "One step forward, two steps back." If you did exactly this according to the illustration, you would spell out the word S-E-T.

75 The press baron had put a secret message in the crossword of his newspaper. If you read every other line, the "unchecked" squares in the crossword read CLARE IS NOT SAFE; PLANE TO-NIGHT AT THREE AM.

85 Take the first letter in CIRCLE, the sixth letter in OCTAGON etc. and you will spell out the code word COPIER

95 They are the letters of the alphabet (A to D on the top row, E to H on the bottom), but viewed from the side.

ANSWERS TO PUZZLES ENDING IN –6

6 Connecting symbols of the same shade, as well as symbols of similar meaning (music notation, map symbols, fruit, body parts) gives an arrow pointing to the angel, which is guarding the prize:

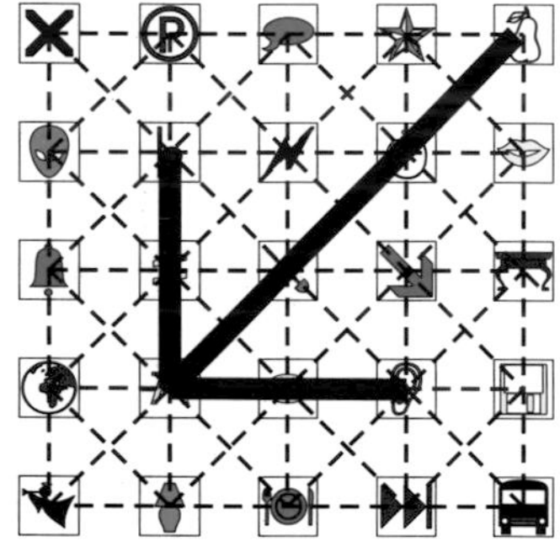

16 Say the phrase aloud and you'll hear the number 425 8980.

26 Push the blocks together in the order illustrated to reveal the SECRET:

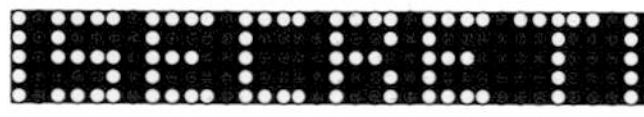

36 Read down each column in turn. The message begins "I wonder how long it will take..." You can read the rest for yourself!

46 Like so:

56 "You must not jump to conclusions. I did not say that my solution would contain a 'fifth symbol', which is drawn similar to an 'F' but with an additional bit to stop it from falling down".

66 Each set of arrows draws out a different letter. If you figured this out yourself, the answer to the question would indeed have been YES:

76 LASER or BUXOM will do.

86 The word VERTEX does indeed take you to the vertex of the pyramid itself.

96 The answers are CON, DON, EON, ION, RON, SON, TON and VON. The first letters rearranged gives VERDICTS.

ANSWERS TO PUZZLES ENDING IN –7

7 Rearranging the shapes so that each square is matched up with its inverse, we see that the room you should go to is number 80:

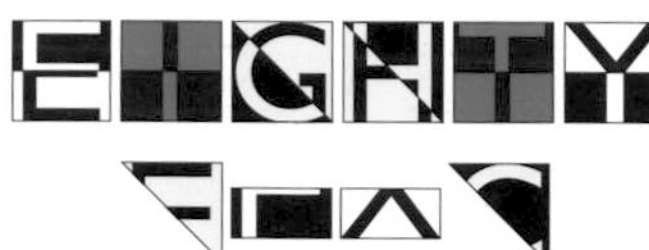

17 Rearrange the shapes into numerical order, then take the first letter of all the names. This gives the word HOPSCOTCH (Hexagon, Octagon, Pentagon, Square, Circle, Octagon, Triangle, Circle, Heptagon).

27 This arrangement gives you the words MEDICAL, DECLAIM, CLAIMED and DECIMAL:

37 The destinations are OPORTO, WARSAW, ZAGREB, DALLAS, CARACAS, and HONOLULU.

47 The message reads WHICH LETTER IS NOT USED, and you have a "P" left over. So P is the answer.

57 British readers will reach the result 1066, the date of the Battle of Hastings. Adding 934 will make this result the year 2000, the new Millennium.

67 Take the yellow clues as an example: the clue "____ stone" is in solid yellow, meaning that the letters inside the yellow circle are LODE (lodestone is a magnetic, naturally occurring mineral). The clue that is in yellow but outside the yellow box refers to the letters that are outside the yellow circle, in this case CAR. Similarly for the other clues: COAL is inside the blue circle, and RED is

outside. REAL is inside the green circle, and COD is outside.

The seven-letter final answer is the anagram of these letters, which is CAROLED.

77 Any word with three letter As will do. The pictures represent PANAMA, TASMANIA, MASCARA, BANANA and CANADA.

87 You can trace the word FLAMINGOES – you need to enter by the lower entrance, and exit by the top.

97 What's going wrong is that the yellow street lights are causing the buttons to look different. White buttons will look yellow, red buttons will look orange, and blue buttons will not show up at all! If the panel were viewed in normal light, it would look like this:

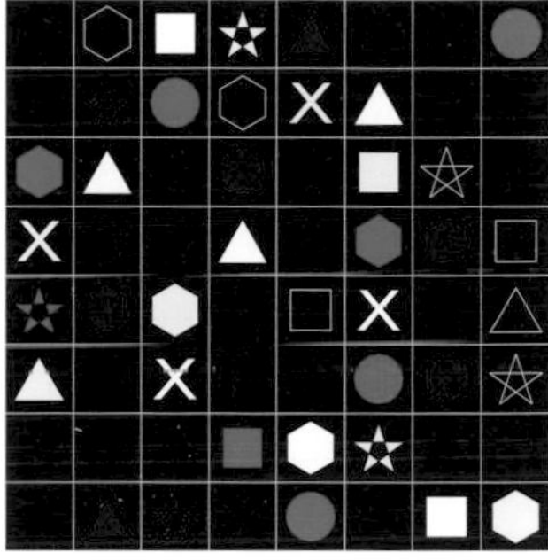

The button to press is the blue triangle near the bottom-left corner.

ANSWERS TO PUZZLES ENDING IN –8

8 If I remove the confusing "inverse" patterns, it's easy to see the black tiles say "What does this mean" and the white ones say "Just skip each time".

18 Just place the blocks in the same order in which they are given in the question. The slightly different grid makes the message "Hi!" visible:

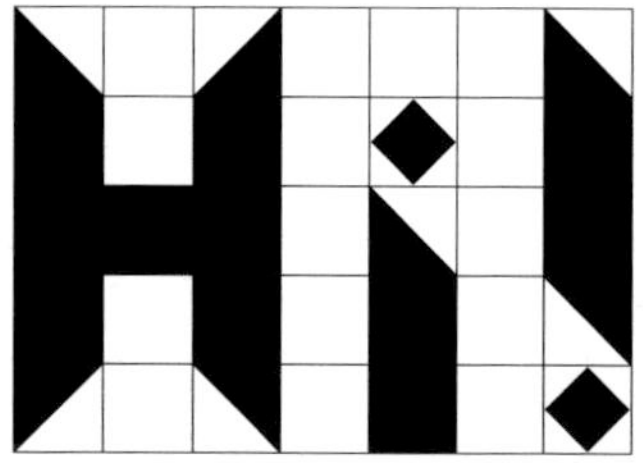

28. You can have a double M (stammer), a double R (smarter), a double T (matters), a double E (steamer) and a double S (masters), but pressing the A twice is a no-no.

38 Starting with the R in CIPHERS, you can spell out RHODESIA. However, technically it would be impossible to fly to Rhodesia because it is now called Zimbabwe.

48 There are eight possible codes, because the piece of glass could be turned over to give another four combinations on top of the four obvious ones. So there's no guarantee you'll make it.

58 The answer speaks for itself:

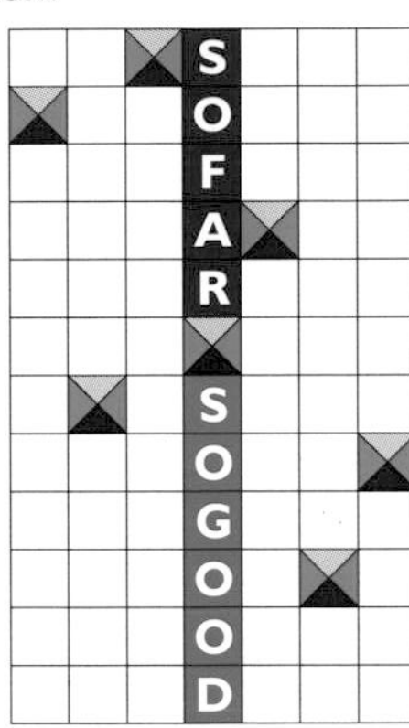

68 SAUCE should go on the white, ALERT should go on the red, MAGIC should go on the black, FEVER should go on the yellow, HOUSE should go on the green, and BREAD should go on the brown. Then, the words you can form include: HAILER, HEALER, HEARER, HEATER, SAILER, SCALAR, SCALER, SCARER, SEALER, SEARER, SEATER, SECEDE, SUMTER.

78 It will spell out RAINBOW:

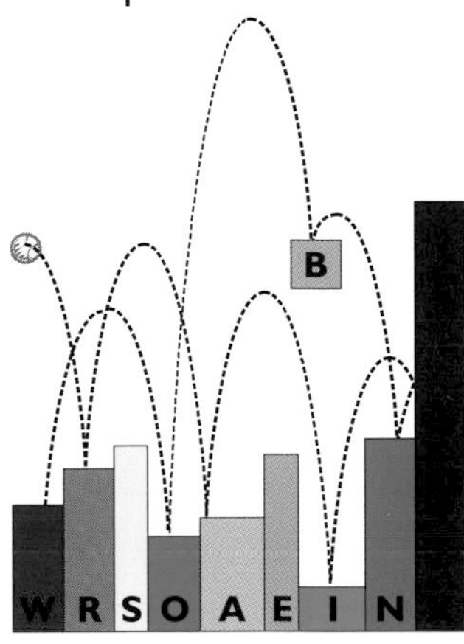

88 Peach, which ends in H.

98 The code refers to the symbols above the numbers on a computer keyboard. For example, SHIFT + 1 is the exclamation mark, SHIFT + 2 is speech marks etc.

ANSWERS TO PUZZLES ENDING IN –9

9 Transpose each letter one position right on the keyboard, so that UD becomes IF. The message reads: *If "typewriter" is not the only longest word using letters from the top row, then the others must be...?*

The answer to this question is Perpetuity, Proprietary and Repertoire.

19 There is one mistake in each line of the "reflection" – either the letters are not reflected properly, or they are missing entirely. Taking these letters and putting them together gives the message "Each line has an error".

29 The letters M, T, Y, O, P, B, R, G and W have been replaced by Magenta, Turquoise, Yellow, Orange, Purple, Blue, Red, Green, and White squares respectively. The I and V squares were already revealed in the question, but these would have been Indigo and Violet as well! Here is how the full crossword would look:

39 Fitting all the pieces together like a jigsaw, and then reading down the column, shows that you need to wear a carnation:

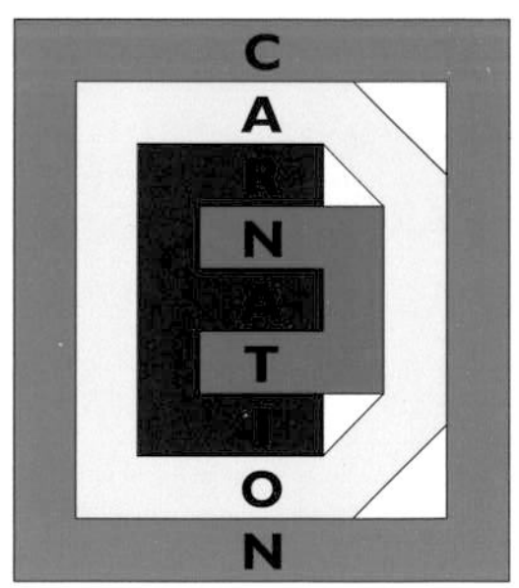

49 The answers to the clues are RITE, NINE, BEEN and BEST. When entered into the grid as shown, you end up with nine letters that can be anagrammed to give the surname BERNSTEIN.

59 The pieces, when joined together, do actually form the word CODEWORD.

69

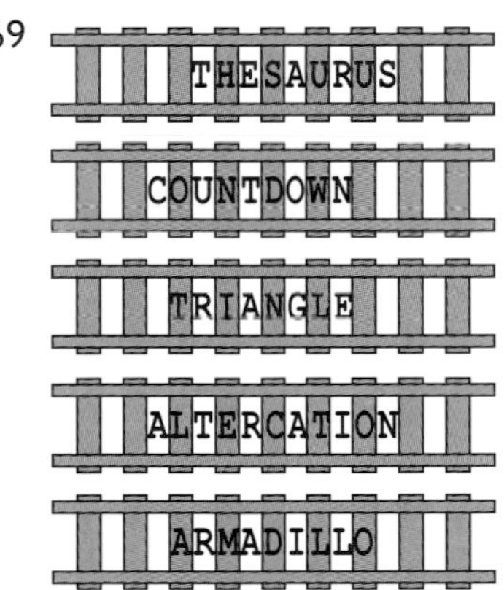

79 If you write the word SECRET down the middle of the page, you will see a set of longer words being formed: for example, PAR(S)LEY.

89 Take the first red letter, then the first blue letter, then the second red letter, etc. The message reads MEET ME AT THE HUT AT TEN.

99 The arrows are pointing you in the right DIRECTION, for that is the word you were seeking.

ANSWERS TO PUZZLES ENDING IN –0

10 Represent each digit with a letter:

Y R G B

The blue clue is better expressed as "green is double the blue digit". Using this, and the red clue, gives us:

$Y \quad Y{+}2B \quad 2B \quad B$

If *Y* is the average of all four digits, then:

$$Y = \frac{Y + (Y + 2B) + 2B + B}{4}$$

$$4Y = 2Y + 5B$$

$$2Y = 5B$$

This means $Y=5$ and $B=2$, otherwise both numbers would be 0, or over 9, or not a whole number. So the answer is 5 9 4 2. The green clue isn't necessary.

20 The correct combination is found if the dial is turned to spell the word DIAL!

30 37053 x 3338 = 123682914. When decoded this gives DAVID x DDDC = BODYCOMBE.

40 There are mistakes at AD (end of tail missing), AE (green shading missing) and CF (whisker missing). ADAECF anagrammed gives FACADE.

50 The middle circle of a dartboard (the "bull's eye") is worth 50 points. Similarly, in the game of carom, the red puck (called the "queen") is worth five points; a red ball is worth one point in snooker or three points in billiards; the red ring is worth between 7 and 8 points on an archery target. Therefore, the red rectangle could represent any of 18 numbers on a roulette layout.

60 For this puzzle, you need to remember that a knight moves in an L-shape, the bishop can move any number of squares on the diagonals, and the king can move one square in any

direction. The words that are spelled out are Chivalry (for the knight); Religious (for the bishop) and Coronation (for the king).

70 Using the answer to the riddle (Rainbow) as a clue, you can put together the words in order of their occurrence in the rainbow, starting with red. After respacing the words a little, you get the message "Meet Chinaman by law court, Room ten. Don a green anorak instead".

80 The word is MISCHIEF. The enemy agent was sneaky by turning the M upside down.

90 16 = 16th letter of the alphabet = P = pea. Similarly, 10 = J = Jay, 2 = B = Bee, and 20 = T = Tea.

Because 21 = U, I should run out the door as quickly as I can – because he's saying "I want to eat **you**."

100 The uncensored message would read THE END OF THE BOOK IS NIGH.

ABOUT THE AUTHOR

David J. Bodycombe was born in Darlington, England, in 1973. Over nine years his creations have appeared in various magazines and newspapers, and on television and radio.

For five years, he was one of the games creators for the UK Channel Four programme *The Crystal Maze*. He also devised some of the virtual reality games seen on the childrens BBC game show *Sub Zero*.

On BBC Radio 4, he has appeared on the problem solving programme *Puzzle Panel*, and is also the researcher and question setter for the treasure hunt game *X Marks the Spot*.

In the 1998 Mind Sports Olympiad, David won a Silver medal in Brainteaser Design, and scored equal highest in the Creative Thinking World Championships.

He has written, edited and designed other puzzle books, including *Lateral Puzzles* and *Optical Illusions and Picture Puzzles*, available as part of this series.

After graduating in Mathematics at the University of Durham in 1995, David moved to Kingston-upon-Thames, Surrey, where he runs a puzzle and games consultancy.

Web page: http://www.qwertyuiop.co.uk/